COLDPLAY LIVE 2

C000002136

GUITAR
TAB
EDITION

Wise Publications
part of The Music Sales Group

London / New York / Paris / Sydney / Copenhagen / Berlin / Madrid / Tokyo

Published by:
Wise Publications,
8/9 Frith Street, London W1D 3JB, England.

Exclusive distributors:
Music Sales Limited,
Distribution Centre, Newmarket Road, Bury St. Edmunds,
Suffolk IP33 3YB, England.

Music Sales Pty Limited,
120 Rothschild Avenue, Rosebery,
NSW 2018, Australia.

Order No. AM979814
ISBN 1-84449-438-1
This book © Copyright 2004 by Wise Publications.

Music arrangements by Arthur Dick and Matt Cowe.
Music processed by Paul Ewers Music Design.

Printed in the United Kingdom by Caligraving Limited, Thetford, Norfolk.

www.musicsales.com

Guitar Tablature Explained

Guitar music can be notated three different ways: on a musical stave, in tablature, and in rhythm slashes.

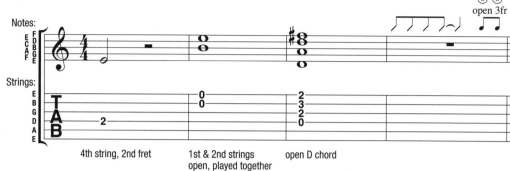

RHYTHM SLASHES are written above the stave. Strum chords in the rhythm indicated. Round noteheads indicate single notes.

THE MUSICAL STAVE shows pitches and rhythms and is divided by lines into bars. Pitches are named after the first seven letters of the alphabet.

TABLATURE graphically represents the guitar fingerboard. Each horizontal line represents a string, and each number represents a fret.

4th string, 2nd fret

1st & 2nd strings open, played together

open D chord

Definitions for Special Guitar Notation

SEMI-TONE BEND: Strike the note and bend up a semi-tone (1/2 step).

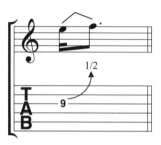

WHOLE-TONE BEND: Strike the note and bend up a whole-tone (whole step).

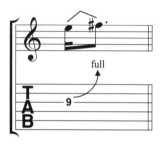

GRACE NOTE BEND: Strike the note and bend as indicated. Play the first note as quickly as possible.

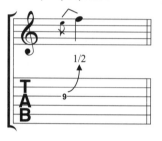

QUARTER-TONE BEND: Strike the note and bend up a 1/4 step.

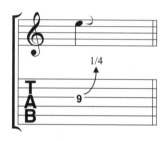

BEND & RELEASE: Strike the note and bend up as indicated, then release back to the original note.

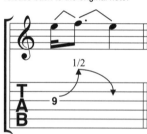

COMPOUND BEND & RELEASE: Strike the note and bend up and down in the rhythm indicated.

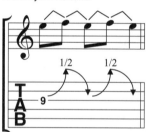

PRE-BEND: Bend the note as indicated, then strike it.

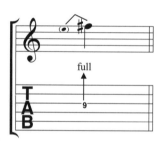

PRE-BEND & RELEASE: Bend the note as indicated. Strike it and release the note back to the original pitch.

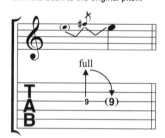

UNISON BEND: Strike the two notes simultaneously and bend the lower note up to the pitch of the higher.

BEND & RESTRIKE: Strike the note and bend as indicated then restrike the string where the symbol occurs.

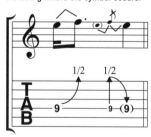

BEND, HOLD AND RELEASE: Same as bend and release but hold the bend for the duration of the tie.

BEND AND TAP: Bend the note as indicated and tap the higher fret while still holding the bend.

VIBRATO: The string is vibrated by rapidly bending and releasing the note with the fretting hand.

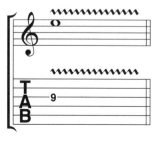

HAMMER-ON: Strike the first note with one finger, then sound the second note (on the same string) with another finger by fretting it without picking.

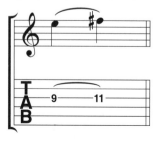

PULL-OFF: Place both fingers on the notes to be sounded, strike the first note and without picking, pull the finger off to sound the second note.

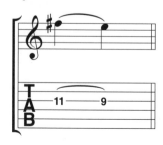

LEGATO SLIDE (GLISS): Strike the first note and then slide the same fret-hand finger up or down to the second note. The second note is not struck.

NOTE: The speed of any bend is indicated by the music notation and tempo.

4

SHIFT SLIDE (GLISS & RESTRIKE): Same as legato slide, except the second note is struck.

TRILL: Very rapidly alternate between the notes indicated by continuously hammering on and pulling off.

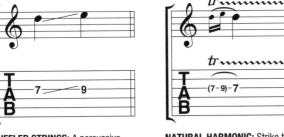

TAPPING: Hammer ("tap") the fret indicated with the pick-hand index or middle finger and pull off to the note fretted by the fret hand.

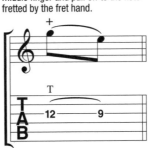

PICK SCRAPE: The edge of the pick is rubbed down (or up) the string, producing a scratchy sound.

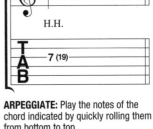

MUFFLED STRINGS: A percussive sound is produced by laying the fret hand across the string(s) without depressing, and striking them with the pick hand.

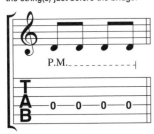

NATURAL HARMONIC: Strike the note while the fret-hand lightly touches the string directly over the fret indicated.

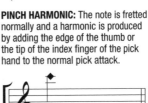

PINCH HARMONIC: The note is fretted normally and a harmonic is produced by adding the edge of the thumb or the tip of the index finger of the pick hand to the normal pick attack.

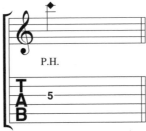

HARP HARMONIC: The note is fretted normally and a harmonic is produced by gently resting the pick hand's index finger directly above the indicated fret (in brackets) while plucking the appropriate string.

PALM MUTING: The note is partially muted by the pick hand lightly touching the string(s) just before the bridge.

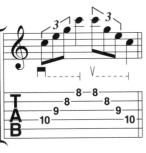

RAKE: Drag the pick across the strings indicated with a single motion.

TREMOLO PICKING: The note is picked as rapidly and continuously as possible.

ARPEGGIATE: Play the notes of the chord indicated by quickly rolling them from bottom to top.

SWEEP PICKING: Rhythmic downstroke and/or upstroke motion across the strings.

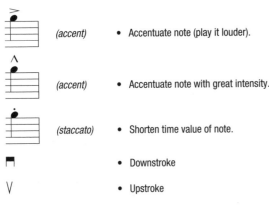

VIBRATO DIVE BAR AND RETURN: The pitch of the note or chord is dropped a specific number of steps (in rhythm) then returned to the original pitch.

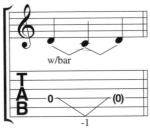

VIBRATO BAR SCOOP: Depress the bar just before striking the note, then quickly release the bar.

VIBRATO BAR DIP: Strike the note and then immediately drop a specific number of steps, then release back to the original pitch.

Additional Musical Definitions

(accent)	• Accentuate note (play it louder).	
(accent)	• Accentuate note with great intensity.	
(staccato)	• Shorten time value of note.	
∏	• Downstroke	
V	• Upstroke	

D.%. al Coda • Go back to the sign (%), then play until the bar marked ***To Coda*** ⊕ then skip to the section marked ⊕ ***Coda***.

D.C. al Fine • Go back to the beginning of the song and play until the bar marked ***Fine***.

tacet • Instrument is silent (drops out).

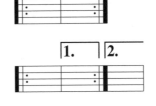

• Repeat bars between signs.

1. | 2. • When a repeated section has different endings, play the first ending only the first time and the second ending only the second time.

NOTE: Tablature numbers in brackets mean:
1. The note is sustained, but a new articulation (such as hammer on or slide) begins.
2. A note may be fretted but not necessarily played.

5

A Rush Of Blood To The Head

Words & Music by Guy Berryman, Jon Buckland, Will Champion & Chris Martin

7

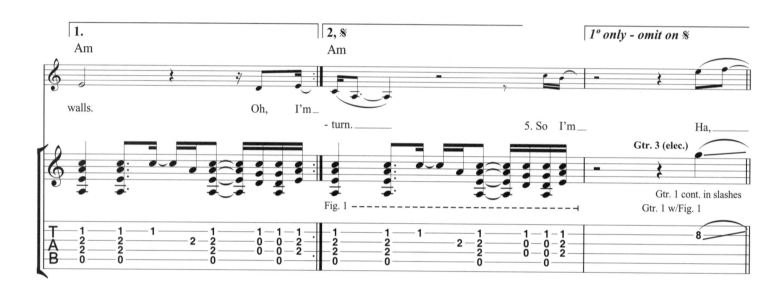

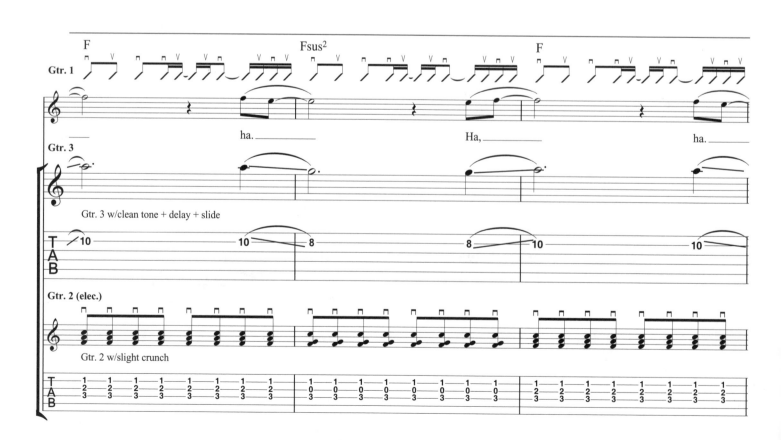

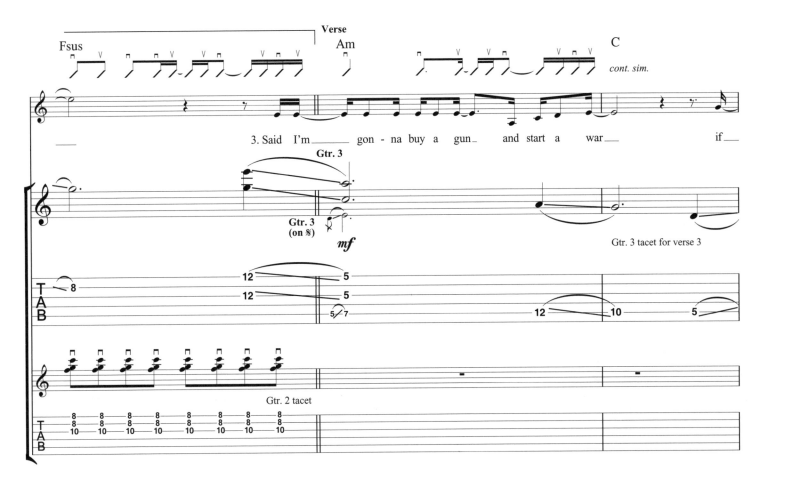

3. Said I'm___ gon - na buy a gun___ and start a war___ if___

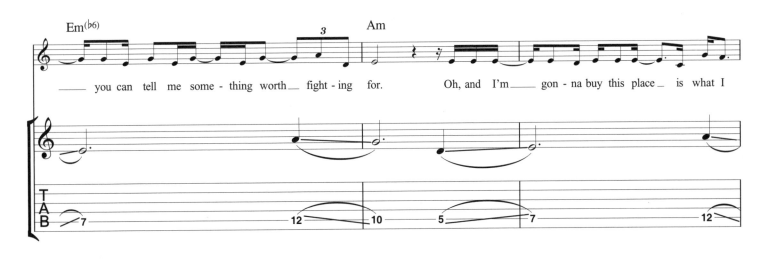

___ you can tell me some - thing worth___ fight - ing for. Oh, and I'm___ gon - na buy this place___ is what I

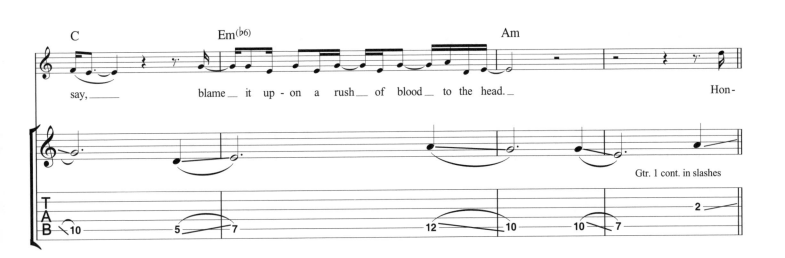

say,___ blame___ it up - on a rush___ of blood___ to the head.___ Hon -

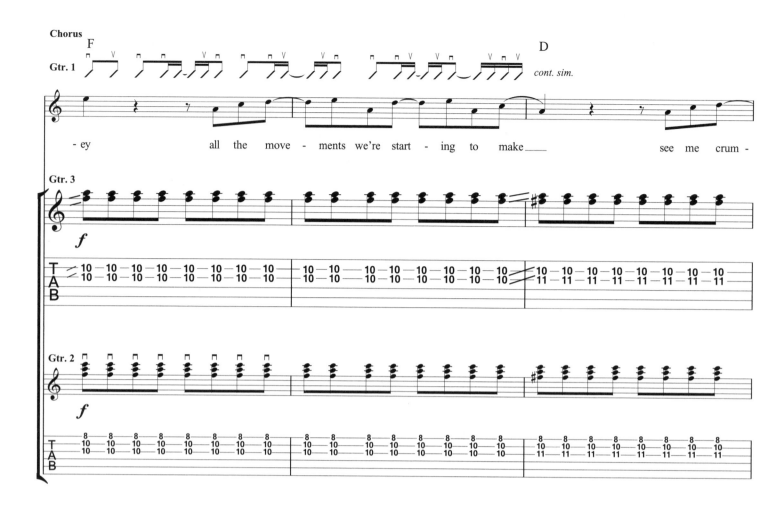

-ey all the move - ments we're start - ing to make____ see me crum -

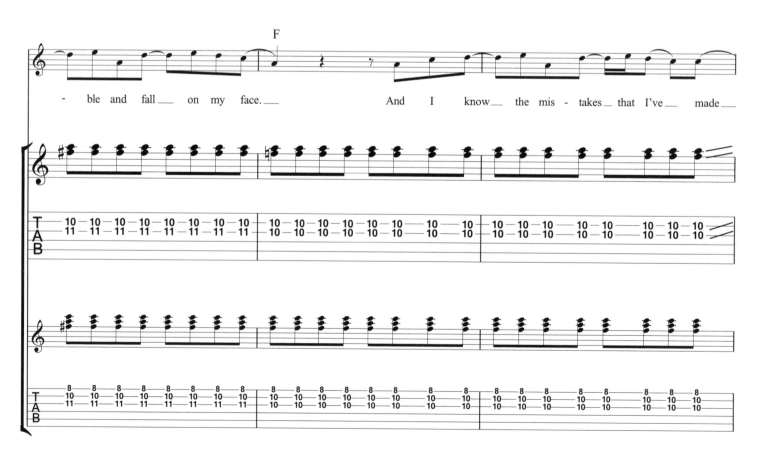

- ble and fall____ on my face.____ And I know____ the mis - takes____ that I've____ made____

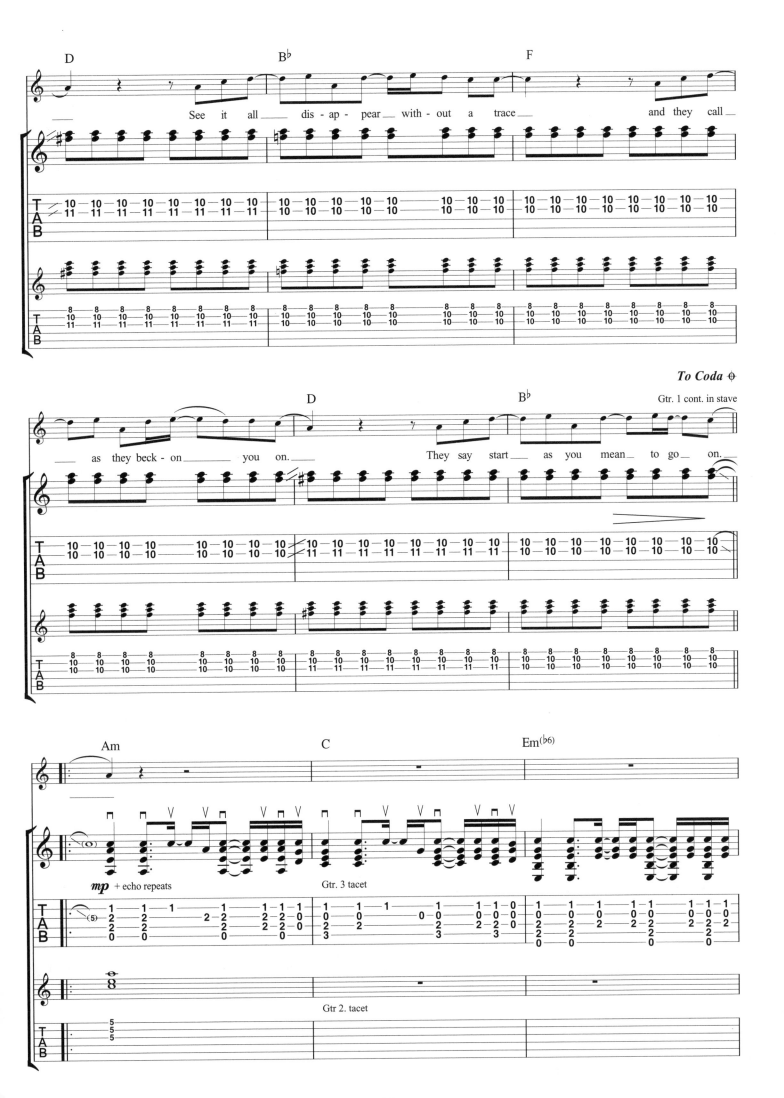

Lyrics: See it all __ dis - ap - pear __ with - out a trace __ and they call __ __ as they beck - on __ you on. __ They say start __ as you mean __ to go __ on. __

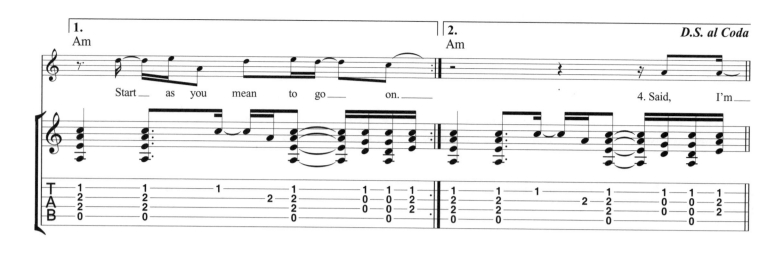

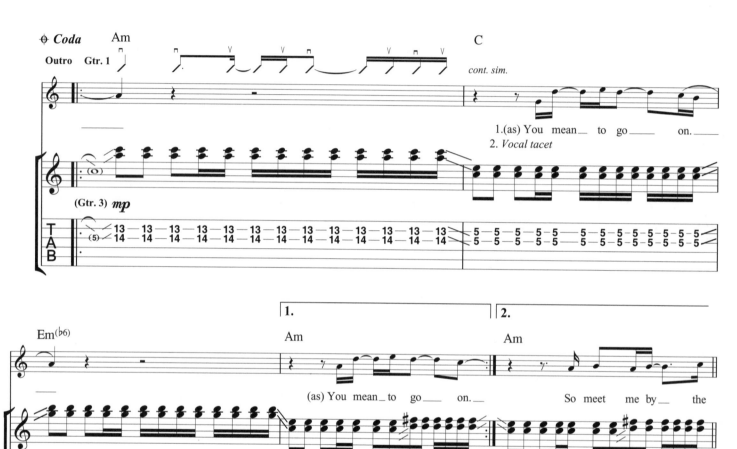

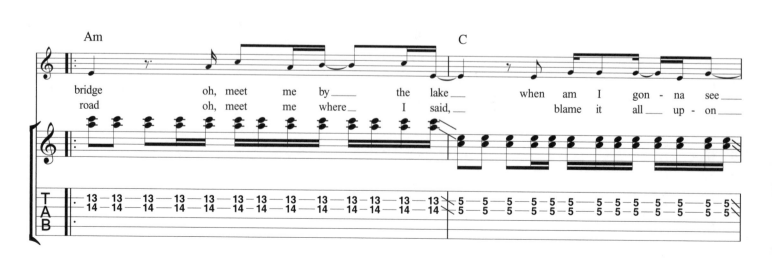

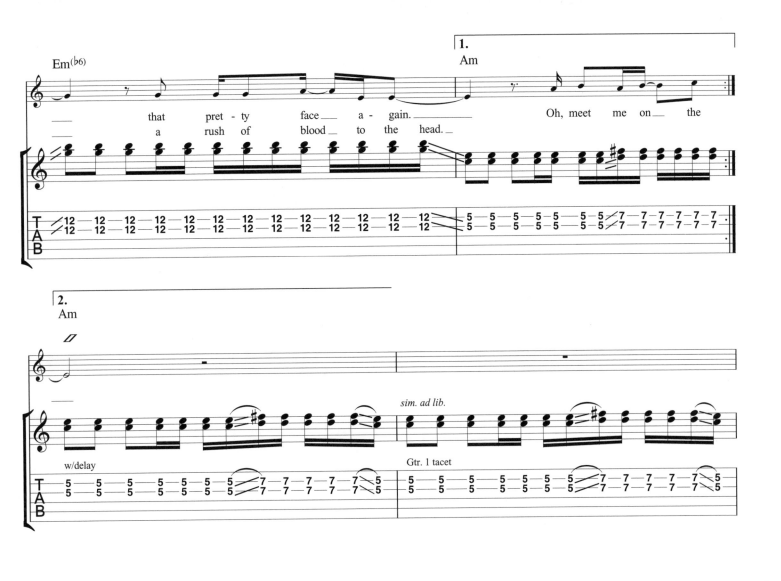

that pret-ty face a - gain.
a rush of blood to the head.

Oh, meet me on the

Verse 4 (𝄋):
Said I'm gonna buy this place and see it go
And stand here beside me baby, watch the orange glow
Some'll laugh and some just sit and cry
But you just sit down then you wonder why.

Verse 5:
So I'm gonna buy a gun *etc.*

Politik

Words & Music by Guy Berryman, Jon Buckland, Will Champion & Chris Martin

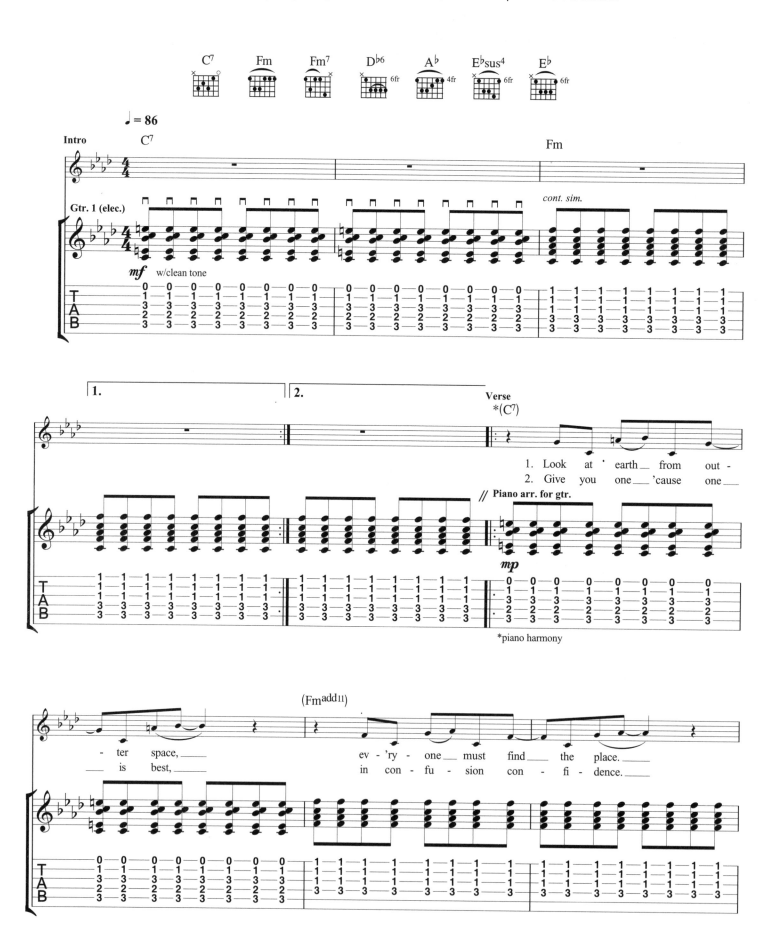

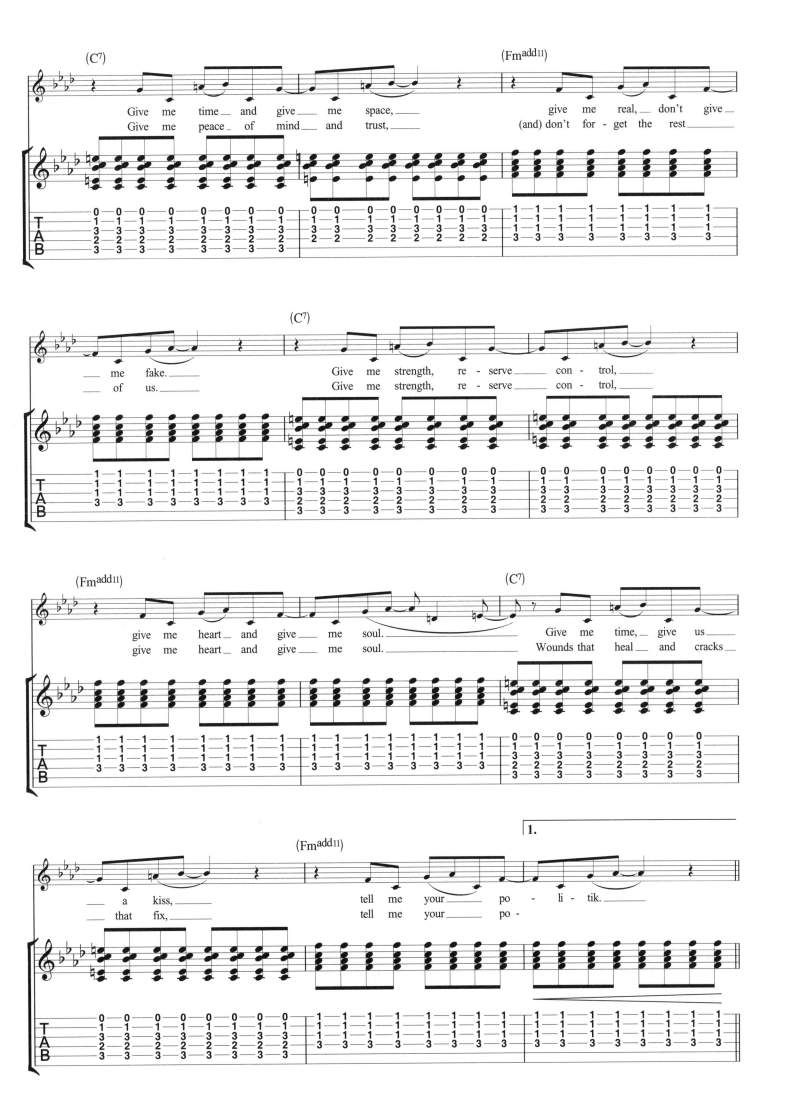

15

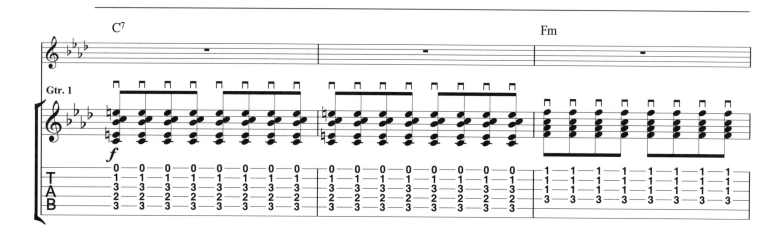

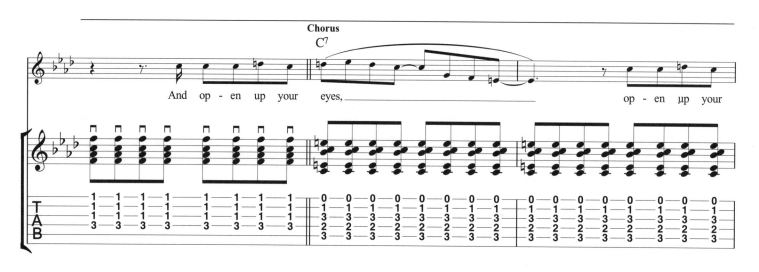

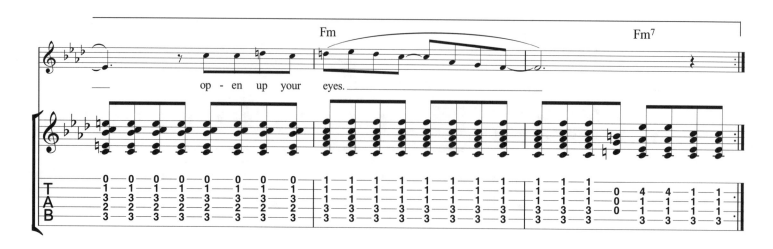

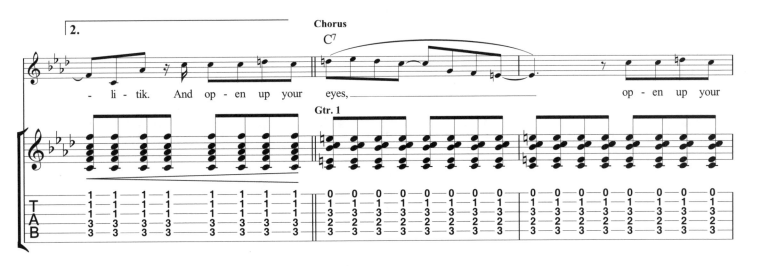

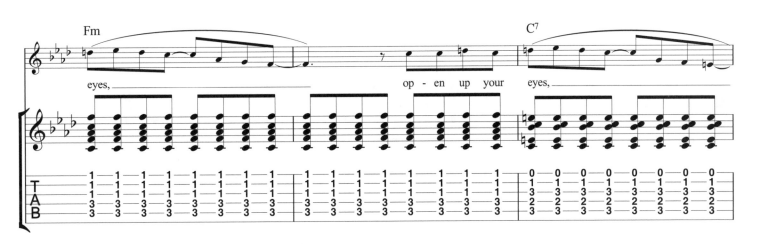

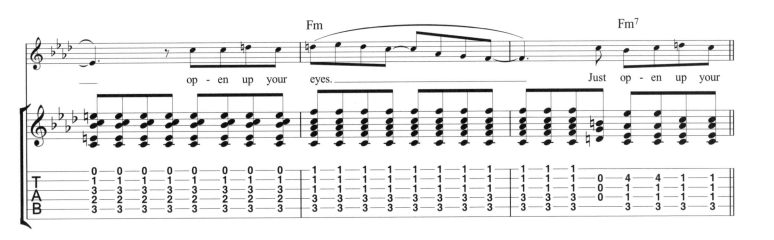

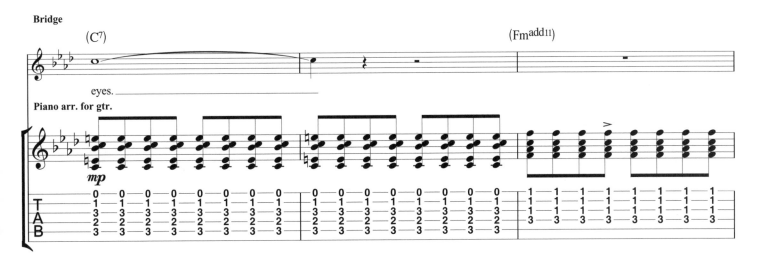

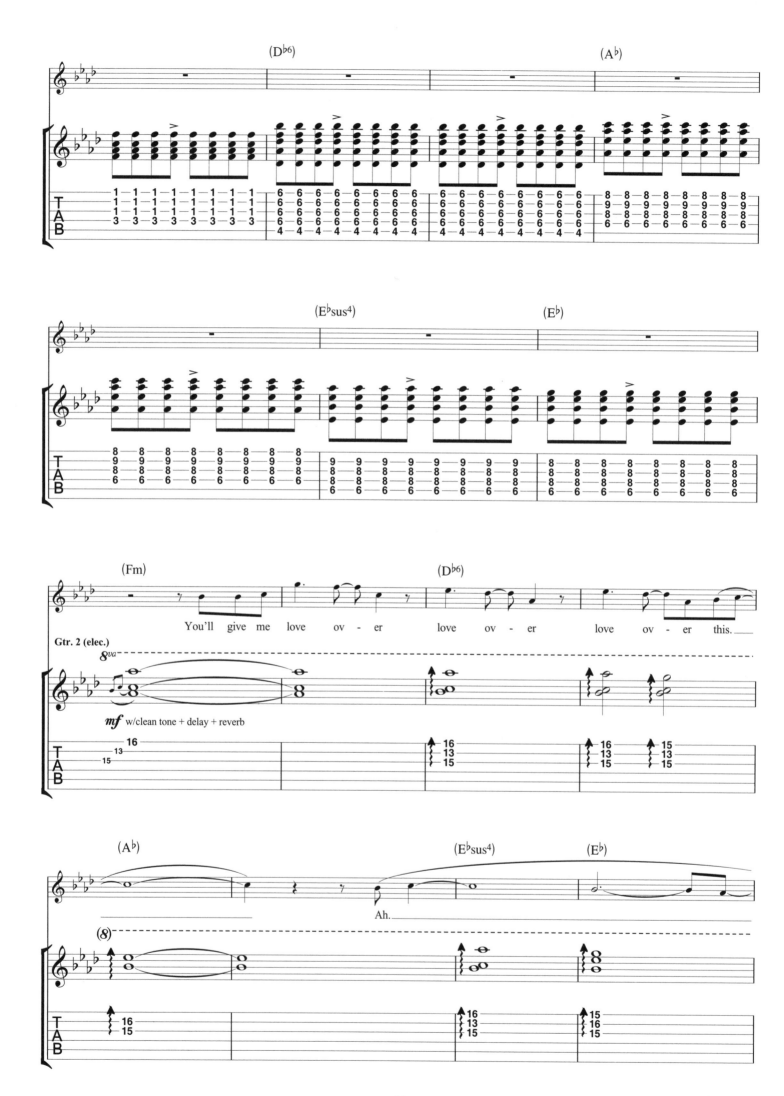

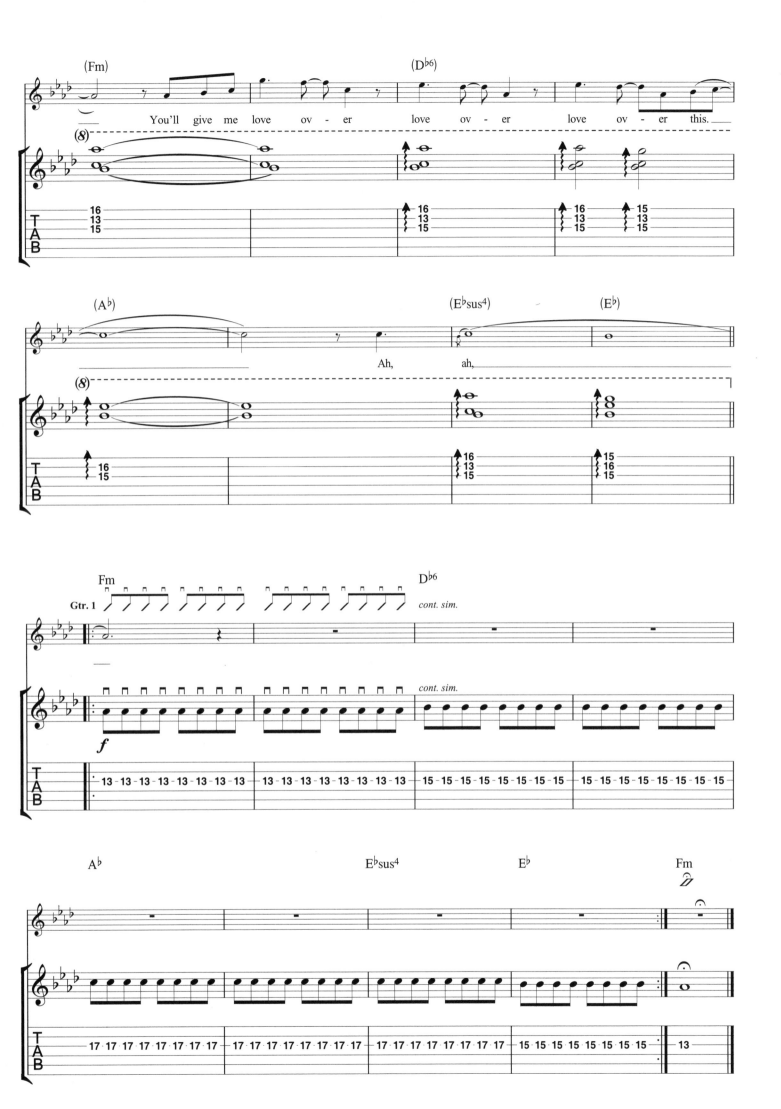

You'll give me love ov - er love ov - er love ov - er this.

Ah, ah,

Gtr. 1

cont. sim.

cont. sim.

19

God Put A Smile Upon Your Face

Words & Music by Guy Berryman, Jon Buckland, Will Champion & Chris Martin

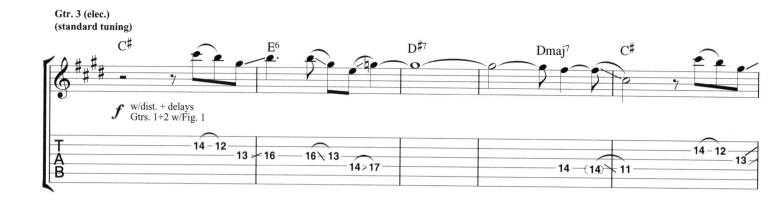

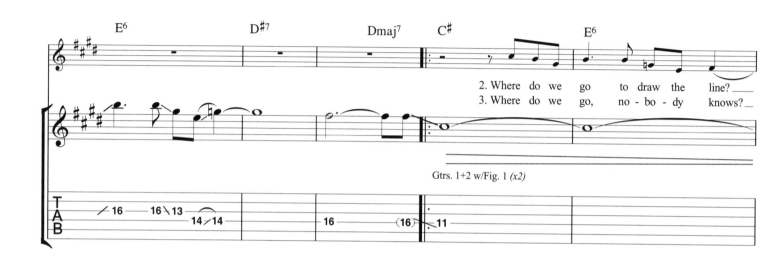

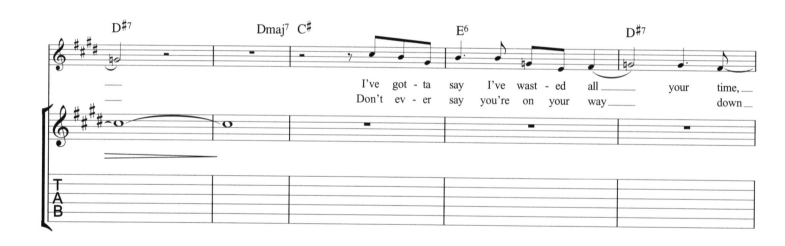

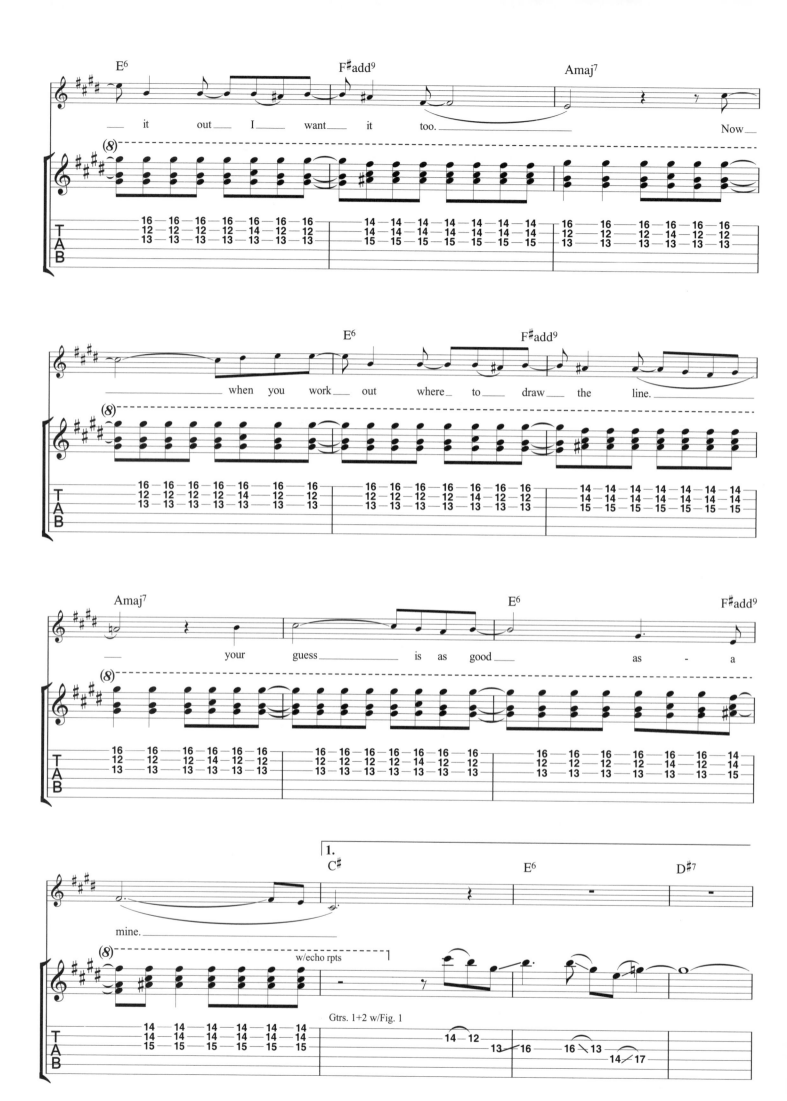

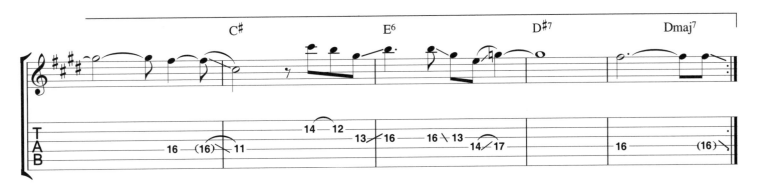

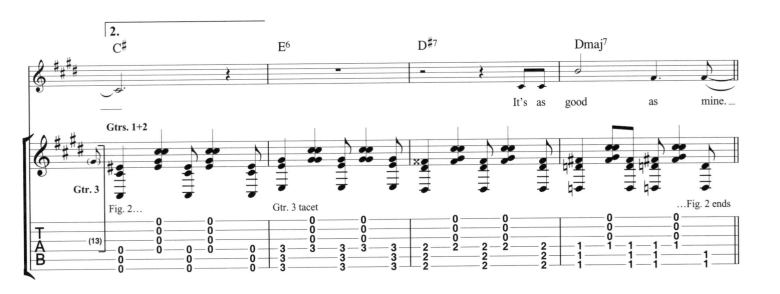

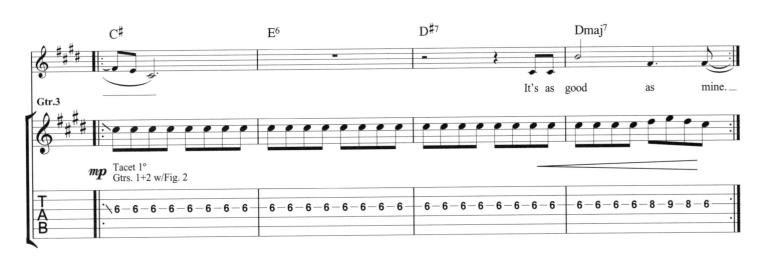

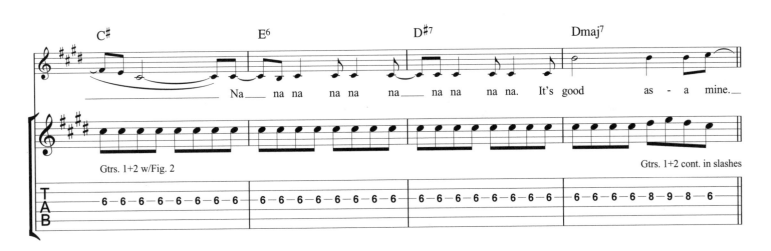

27

Daylight

Words & Music by Guy Berryman, Jon Buckland, Will Champion & Chris Martin

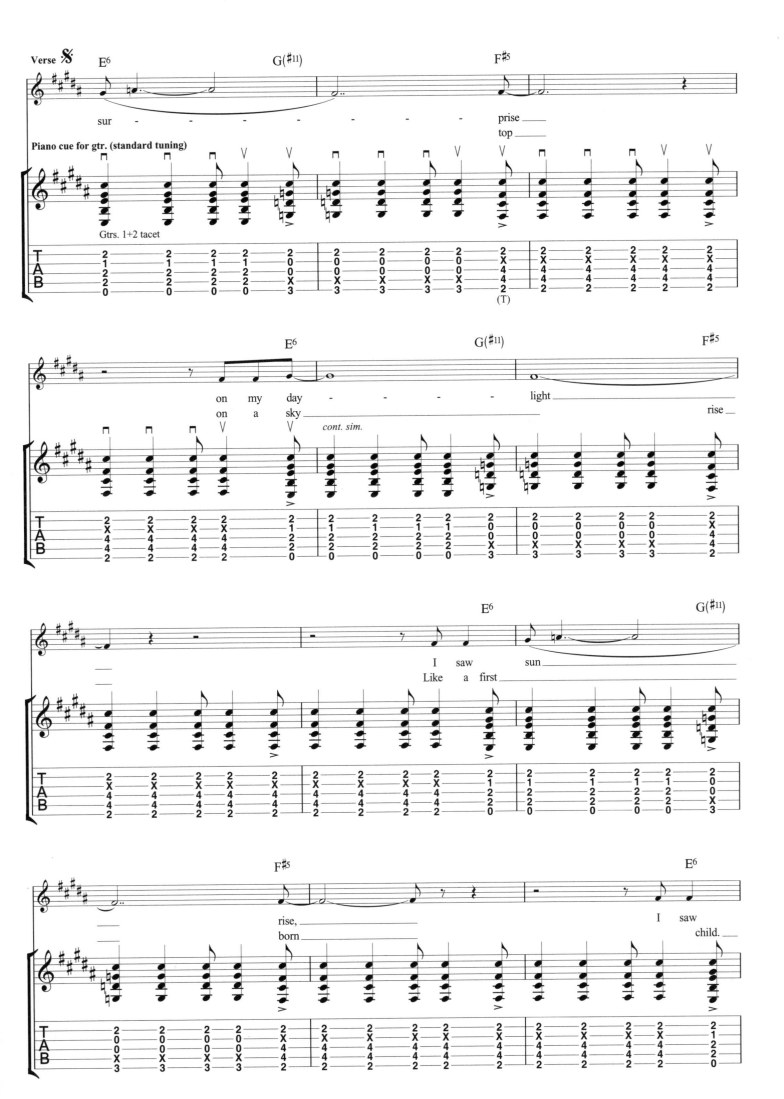

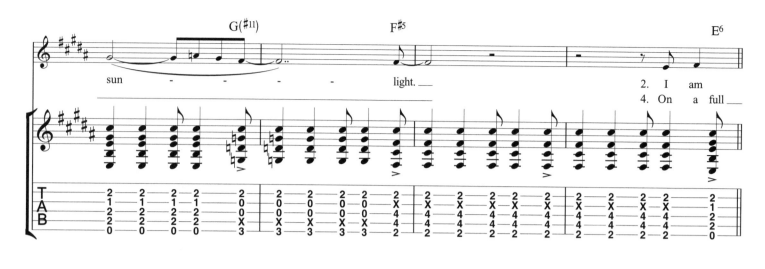

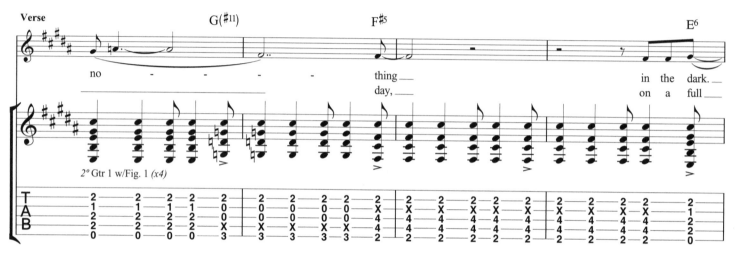

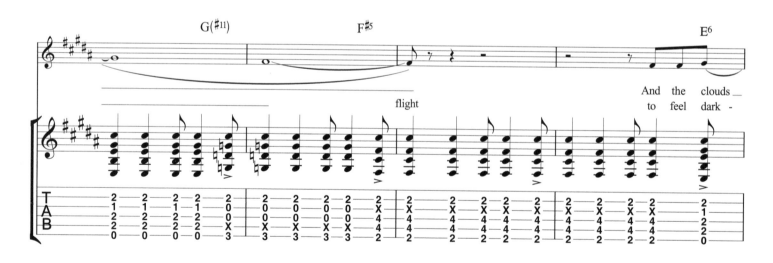

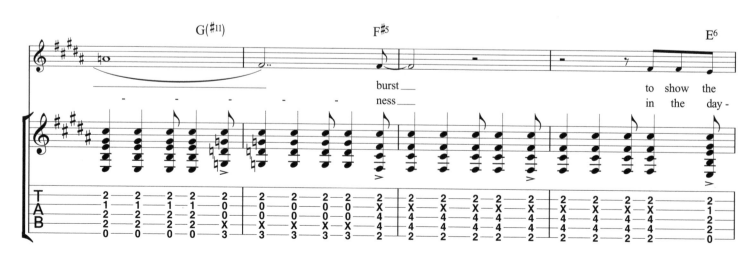

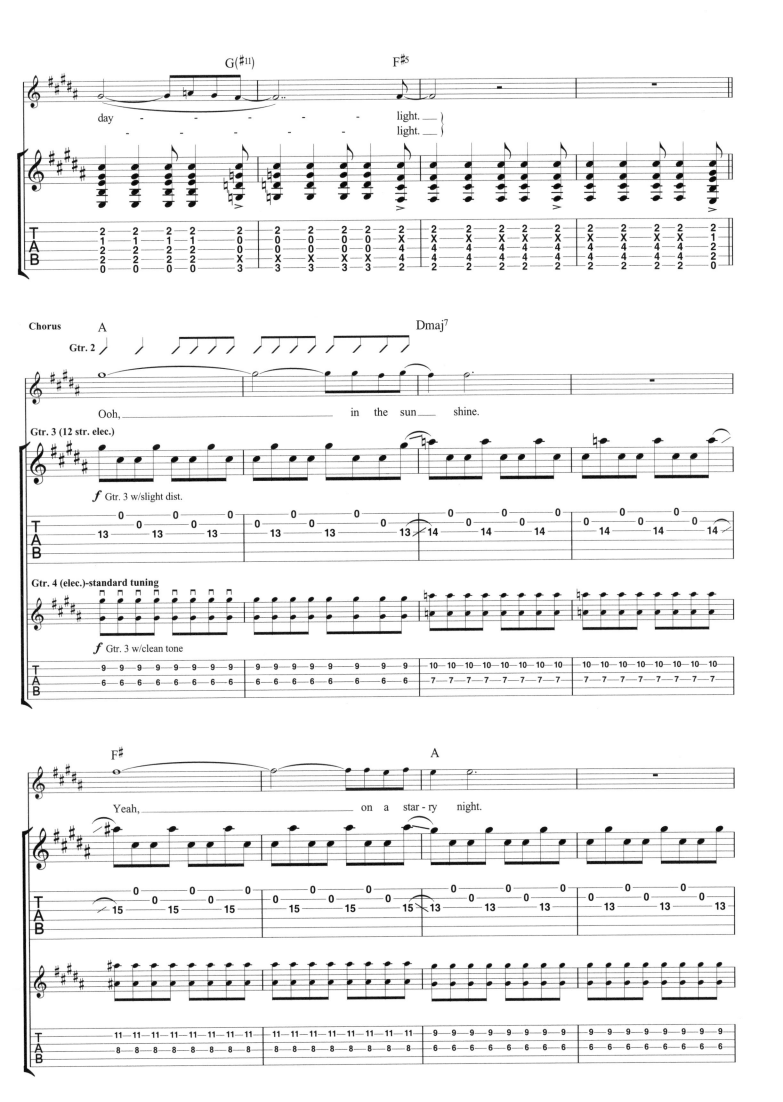

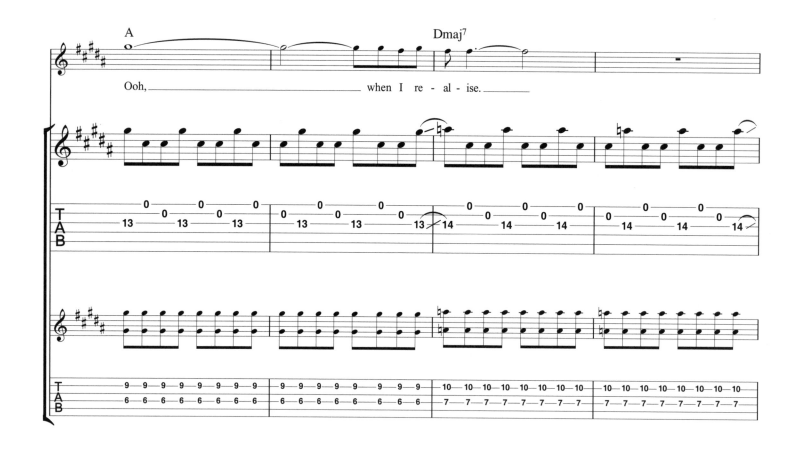

Ooh,_____ when I re - al - ise._____

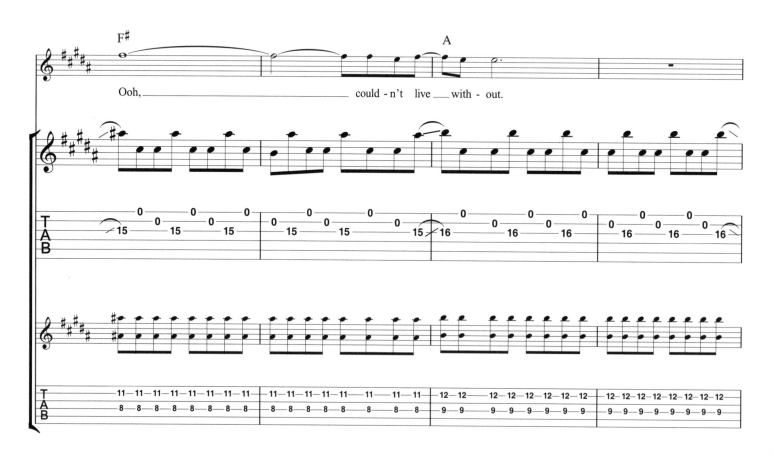

Ooh,_____ could - n't live ___ with - out.

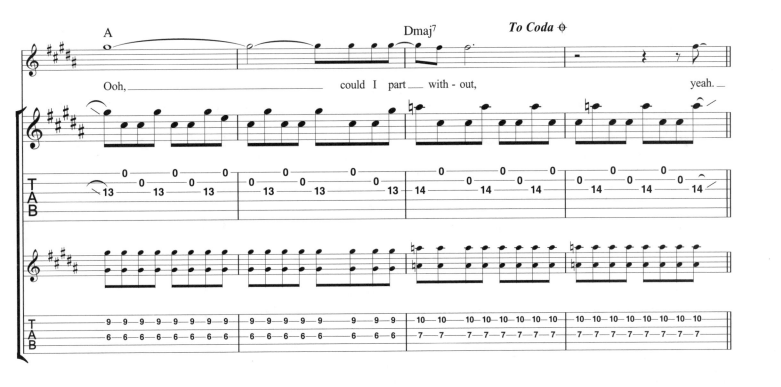

Ooh,_____ could I part___ with - out, yeah.___

3. On a hill -

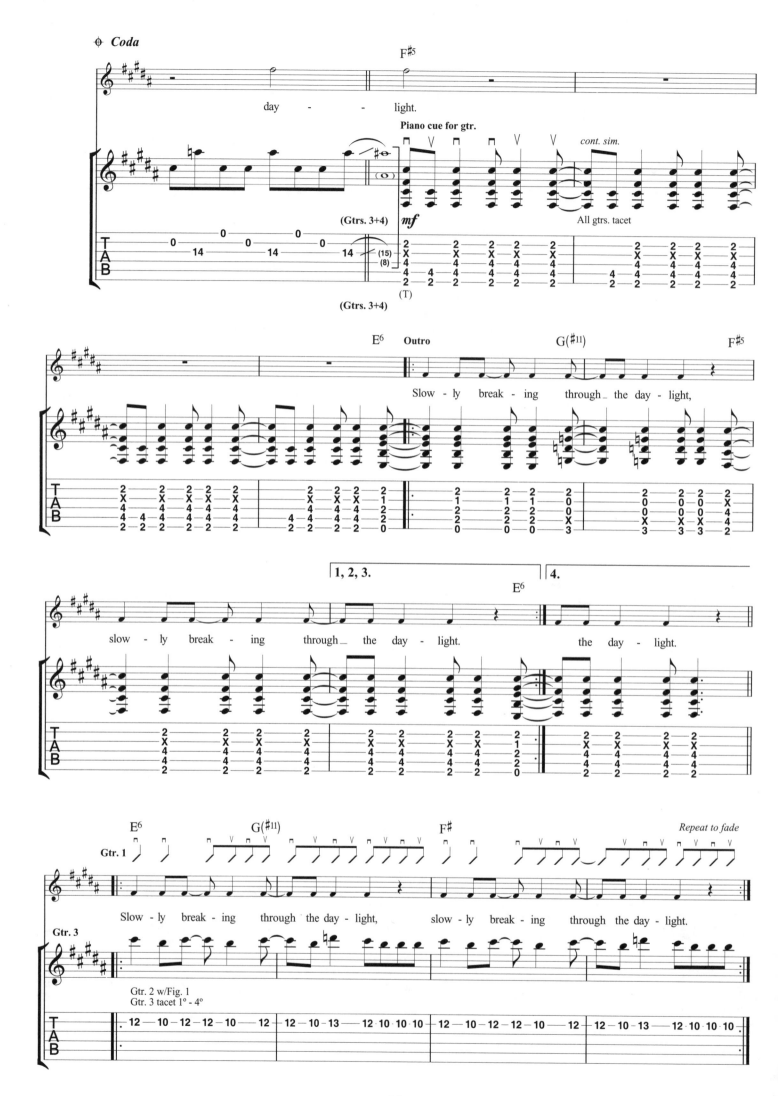

34

Trouble

Words & Music by Guy Berryman, Jon Buckland, Will Champion & Chris Martin

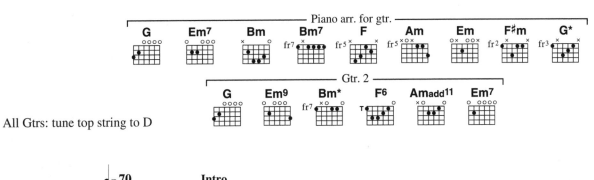

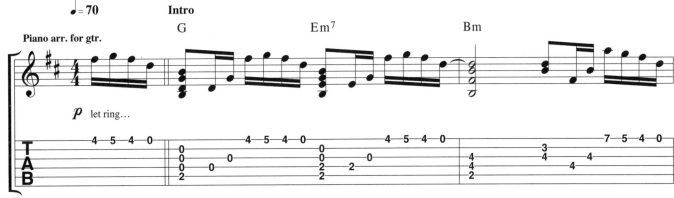

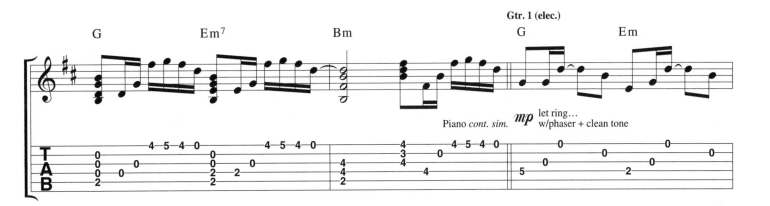

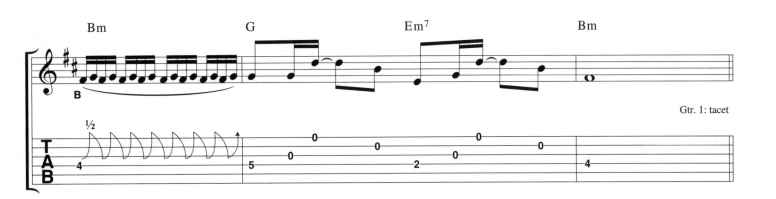

Fig. 2

Fig. 3

Fig. 4

37

One I Love

Words & Music by Guy Berryman, Jon Buckland, Will Champion & Chris Martin

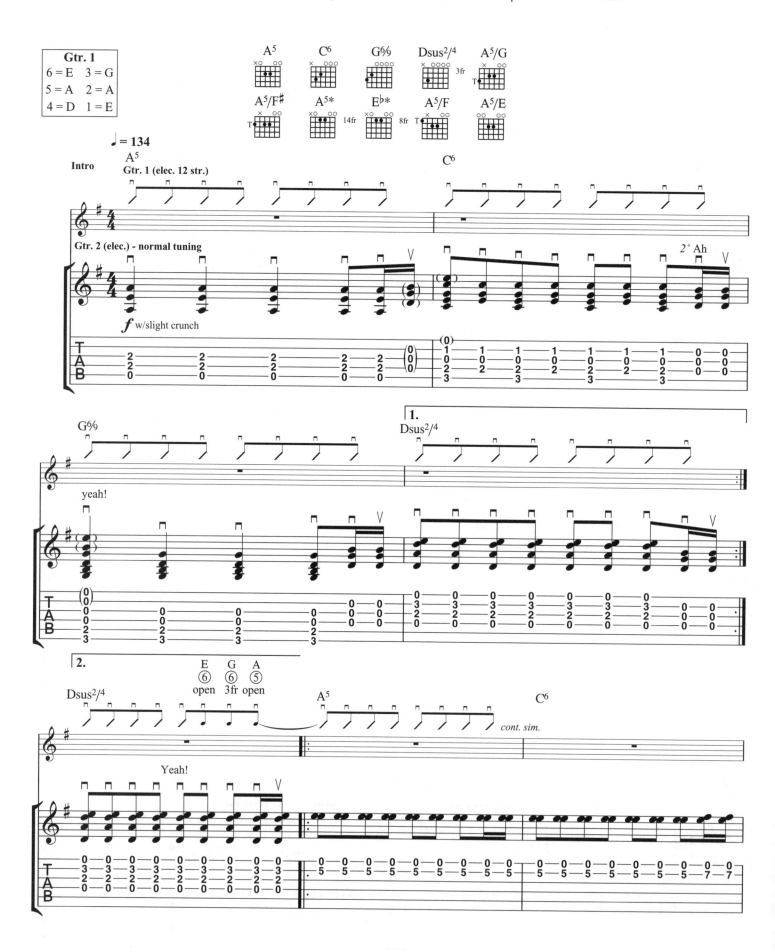

41

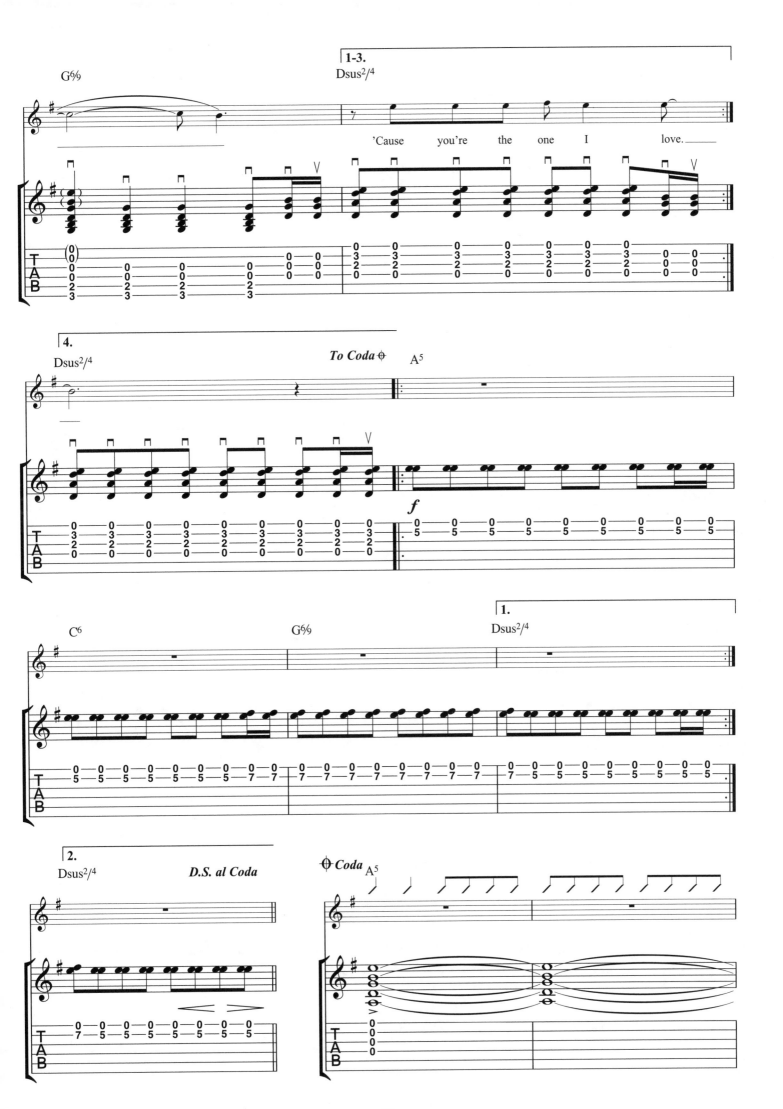

'Cause you're the one I love.

Don't Panic

Words & Music by Guy Berryman, Jon Buckland, Will Champion & Chris Martin

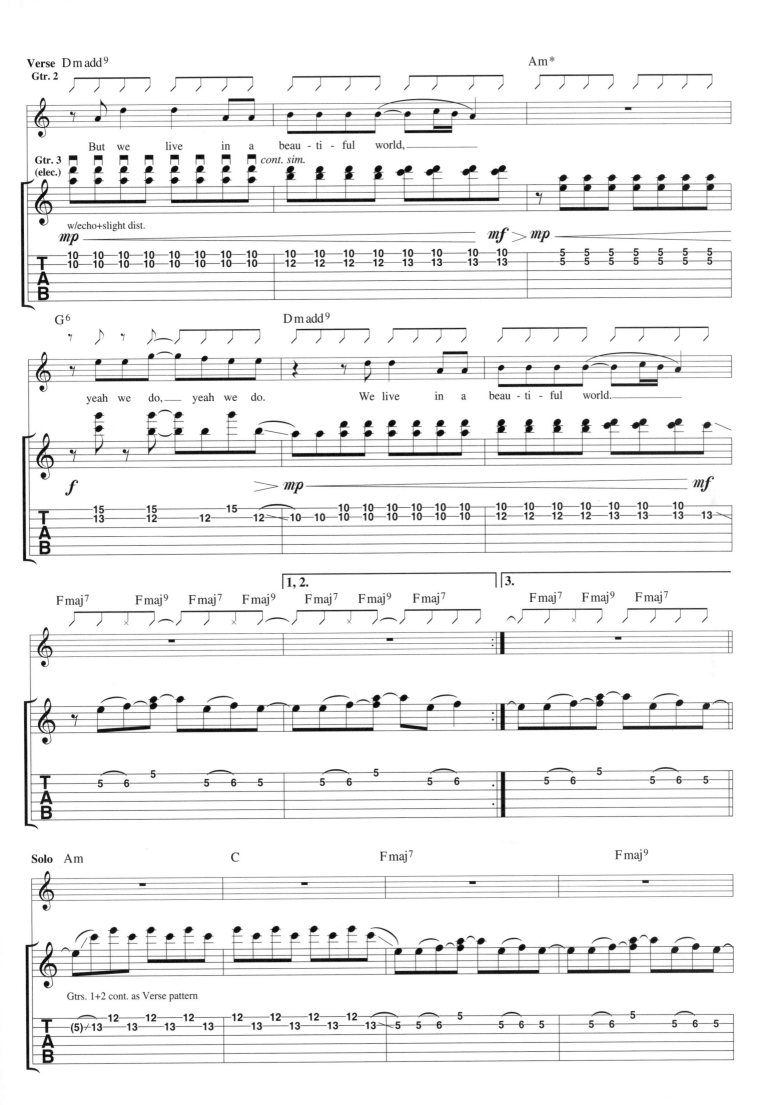

50

Shiver

Words & Music by Guy Berryman, Jon Buckland, Will Champion & Chris Martin

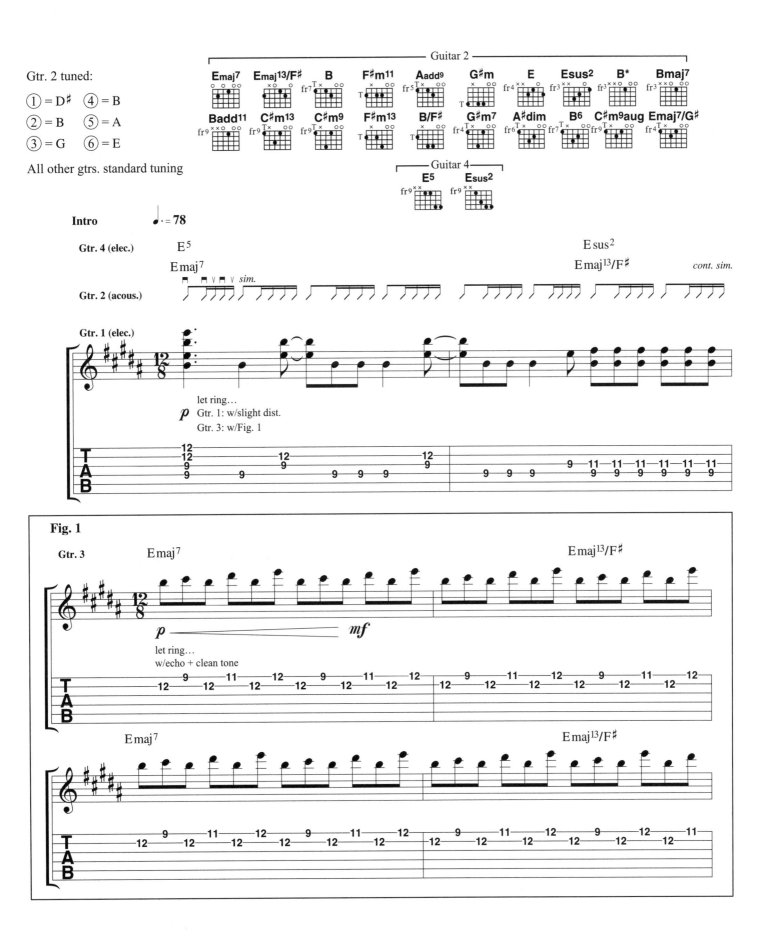

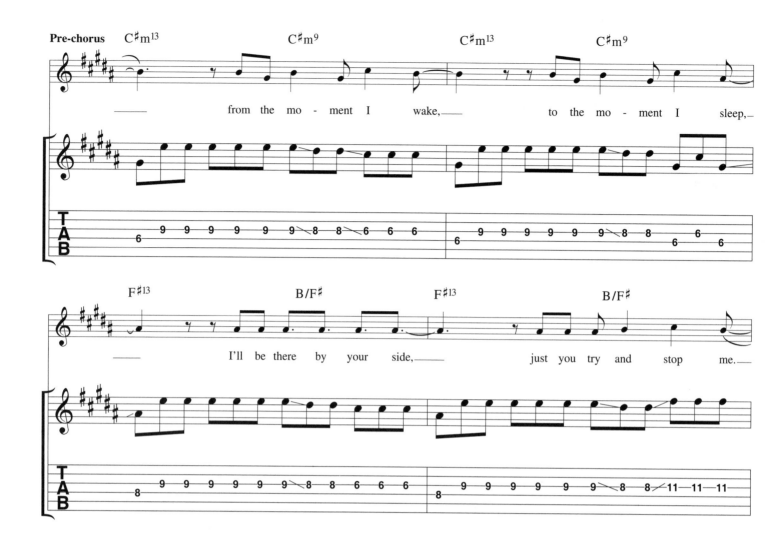

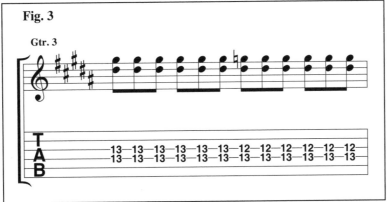

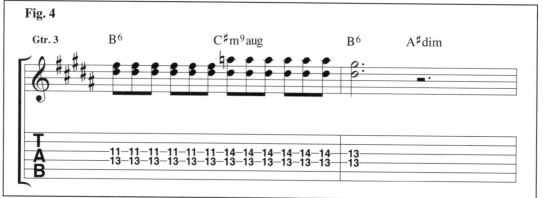

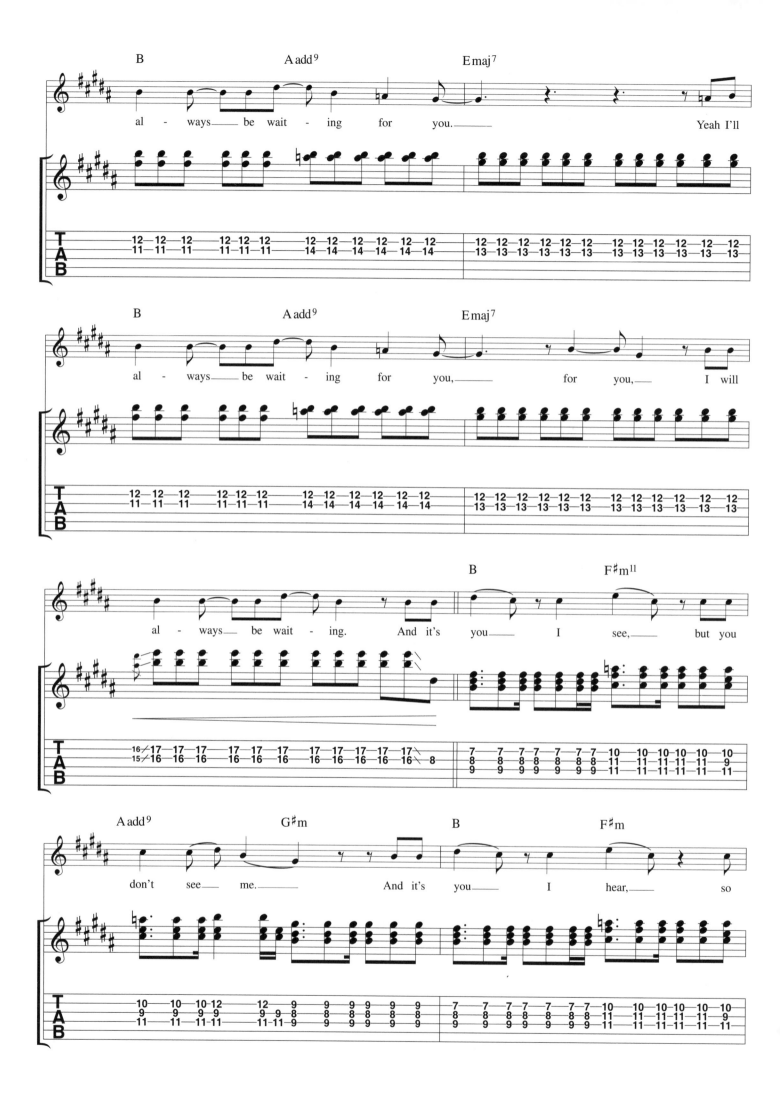

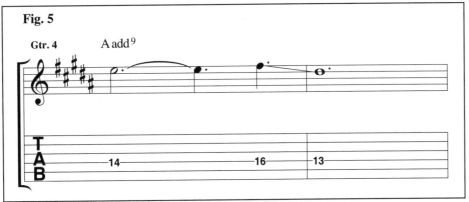

See You Soon

Words & Music by Guy Berryman, Jon Buckland, Will Champion & Chris Martin

ev - er hear this, well don't an - swer that.

Chorus

'Cause in a bul - let proof

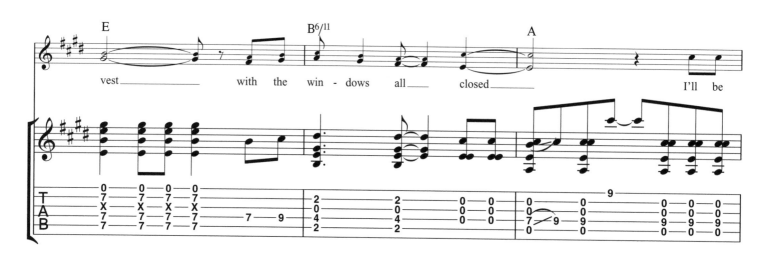

vest with the win - dows all closed I'll be

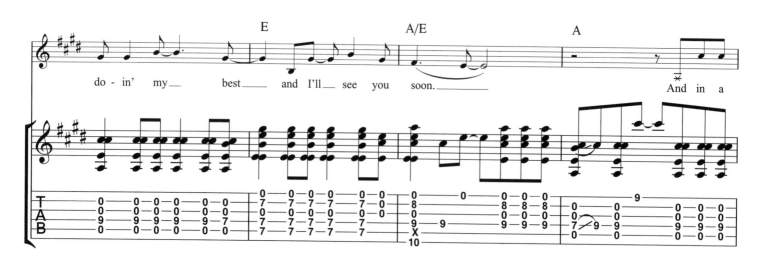

do - in' my best and I'll see you soon. And in a

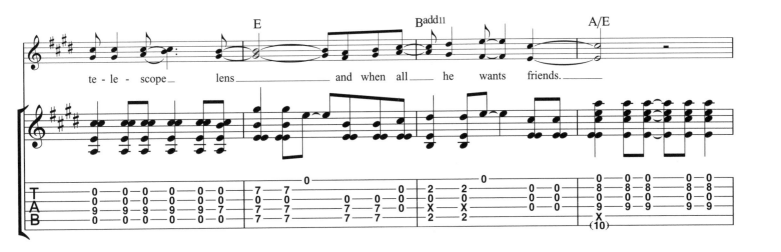

te - le - scope lens and when all he wants friends.

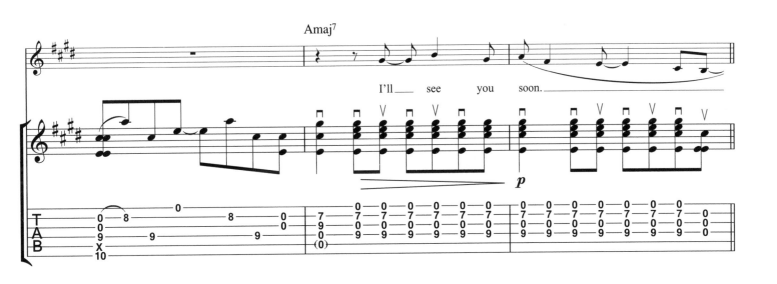

I'll see you soon.

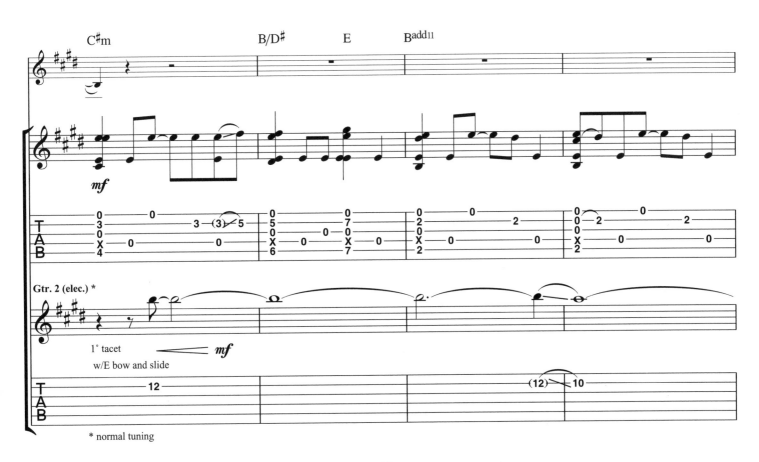

* normal tuning

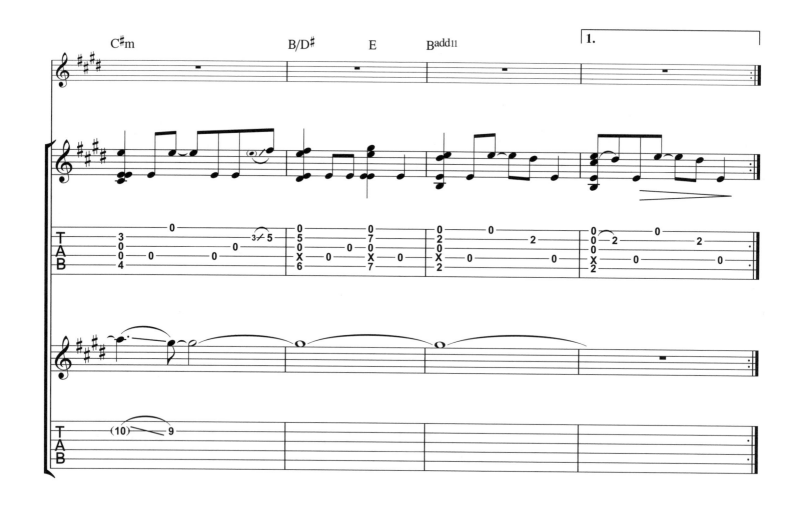

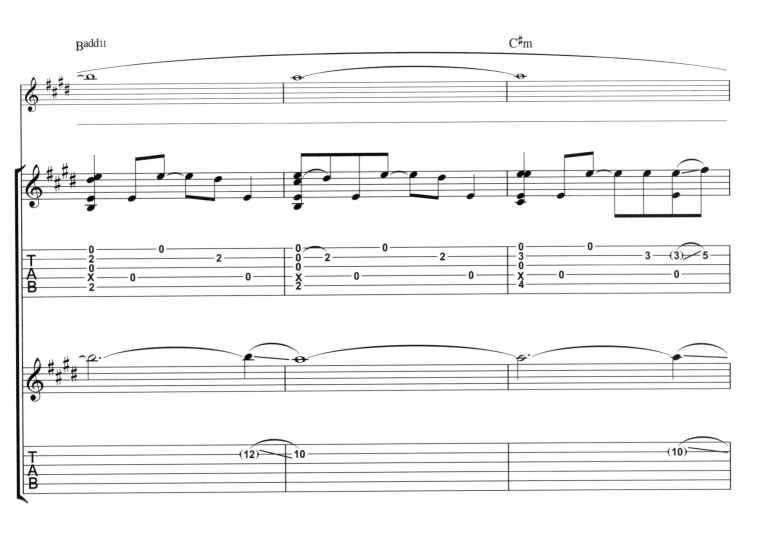

Outro

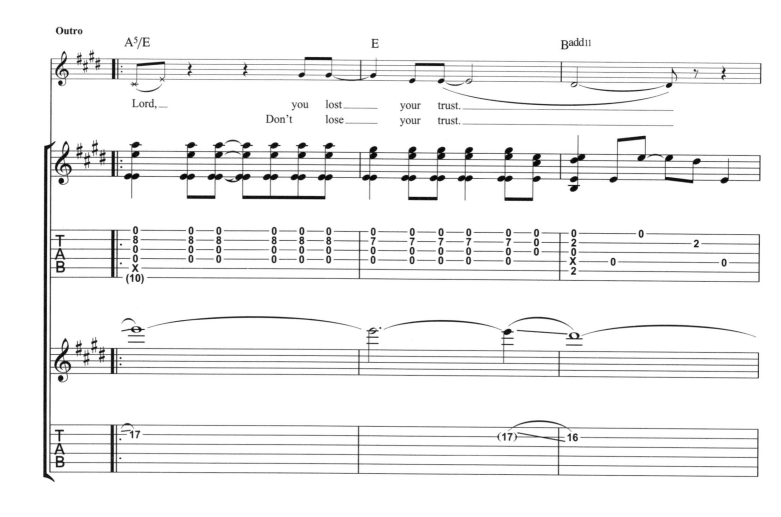

Lord,＿ you lost＿ your trust.＿
Don't lose＿ your trust.＿

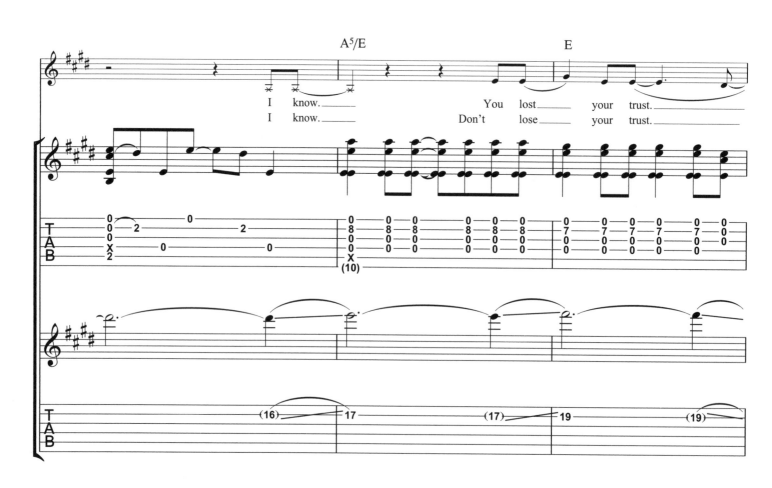

I know.＿
I know.＿

You lost＿ your trust.
Don't lose＿ your trust.＿

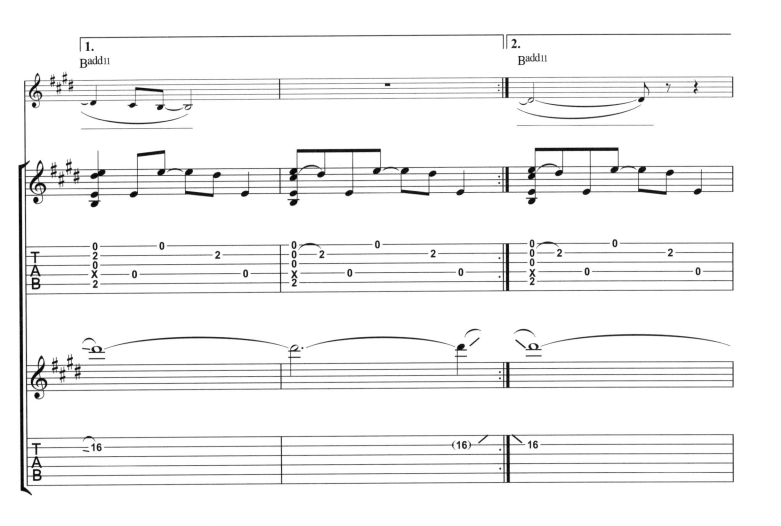

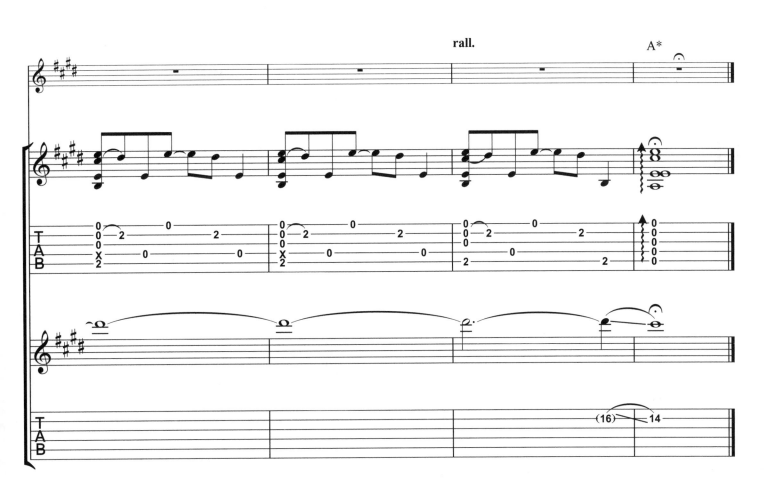

Everything's Not Lost

Words & Music by Guy Berryman, Jon Buckland, Will Champion & Chris Martin

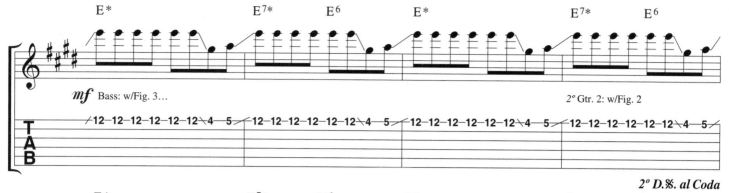

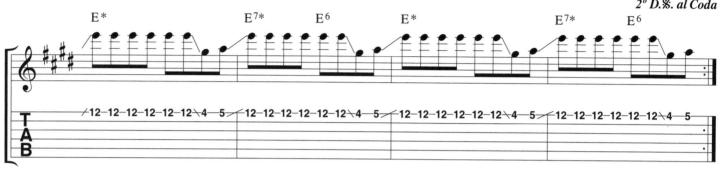

2° D.%. al Coda

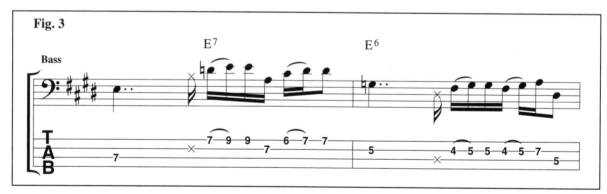

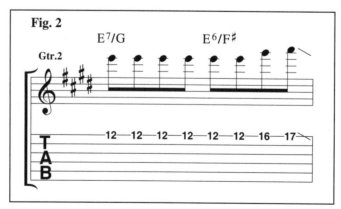

Moses

Words & Music by Guy Berryman, Jon Buckland, Will Champion & Chris Martin

*Symbols in parentheses represent chord names with respect to capoed guitar (TAB 0 = 2nd fret).
Symbols above represent actual sounding chords.

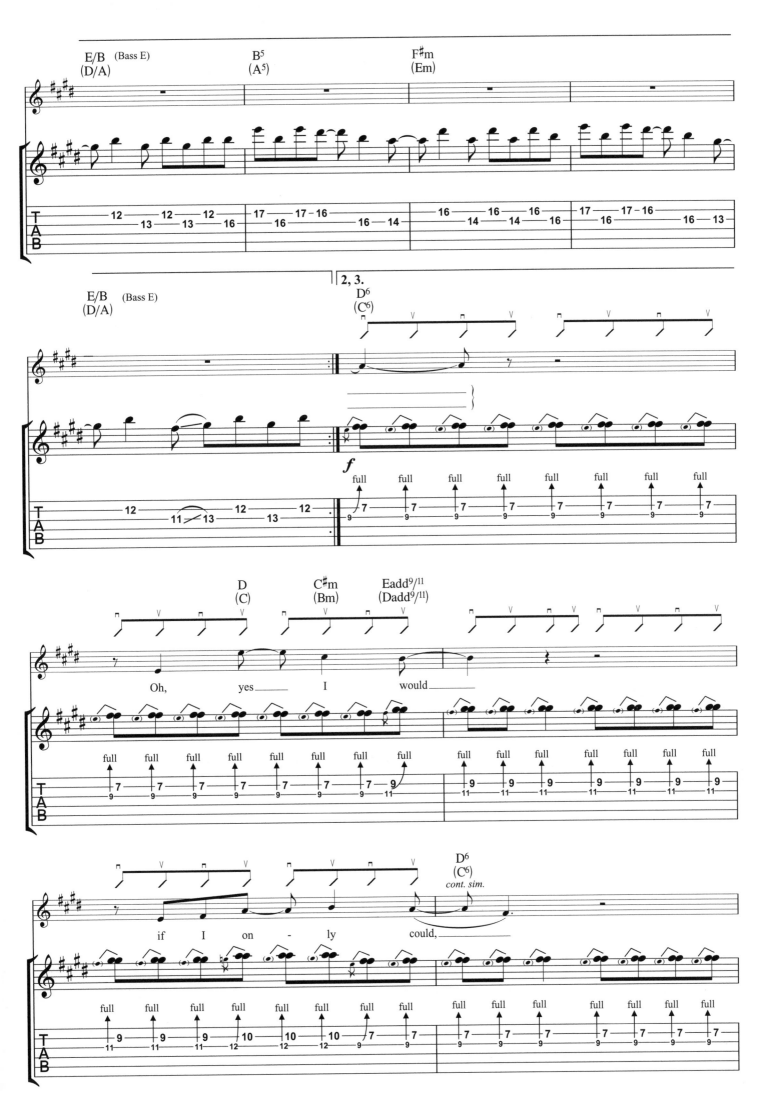

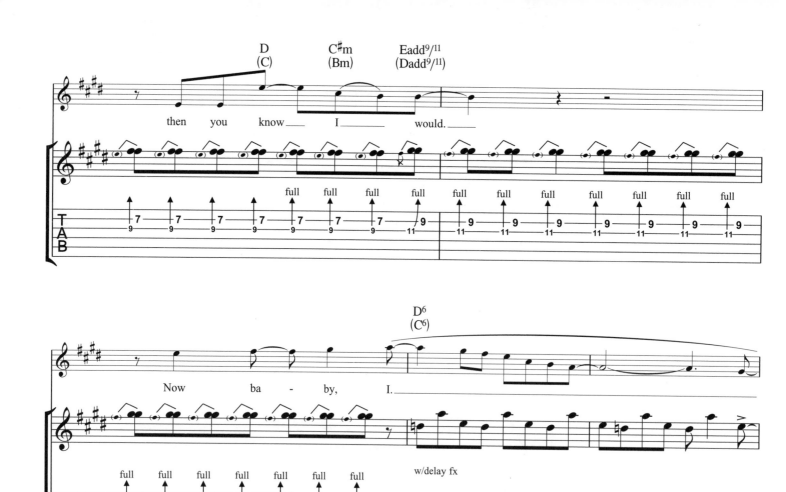

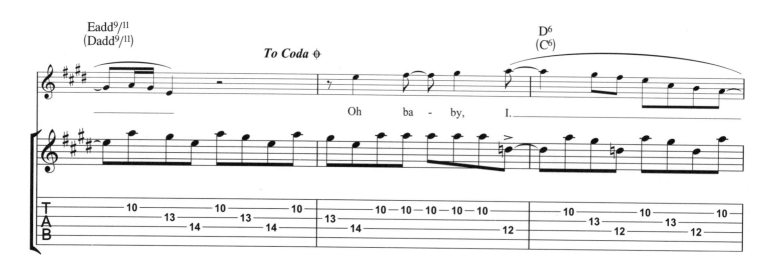

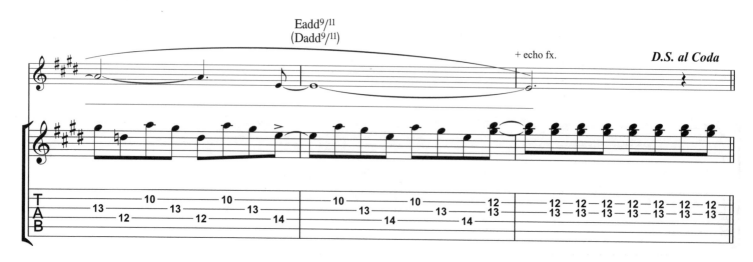

78

Yellow

Words & Music by Guy Berryman, Jon Buckland, Will Champion & Chris Martin

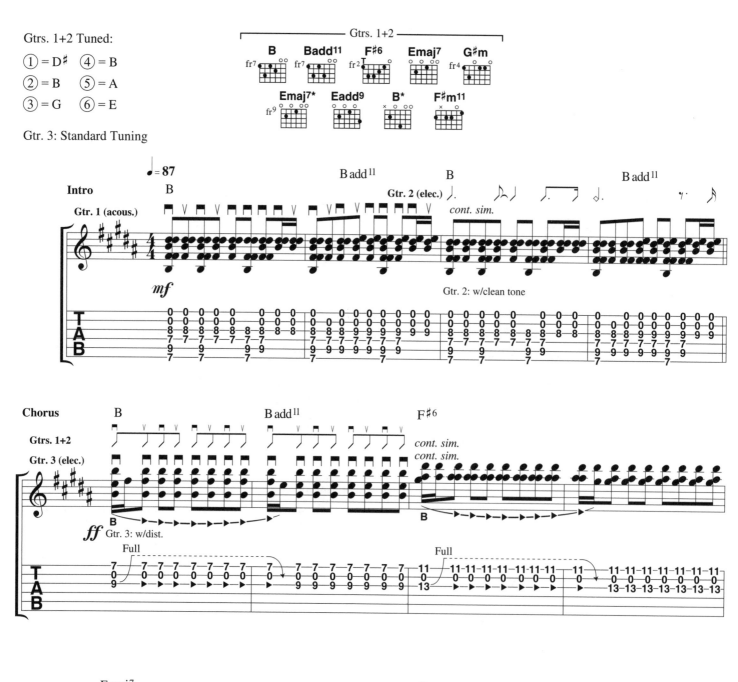

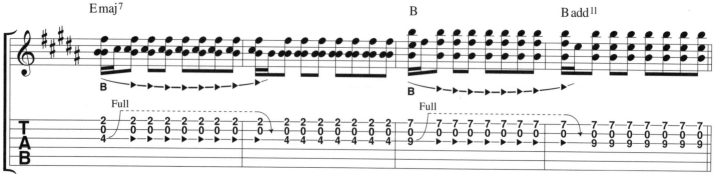

82

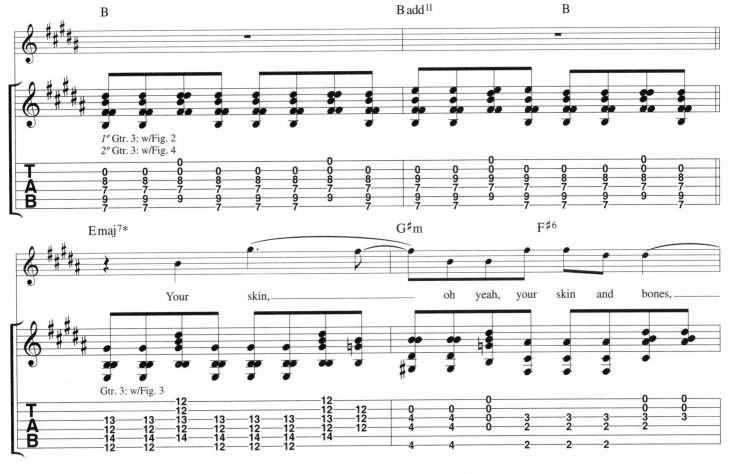

Your skin, _____ oh yeah, your skin and bones, _____

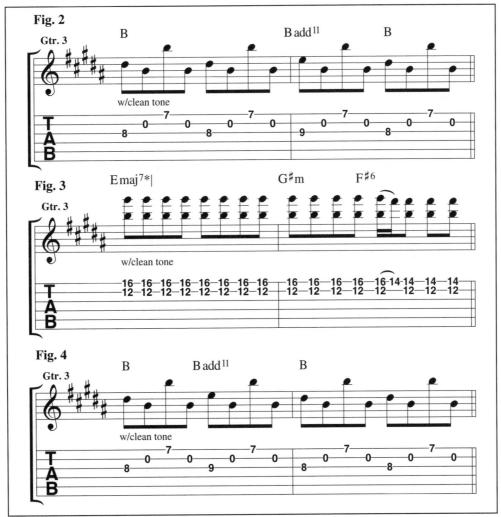

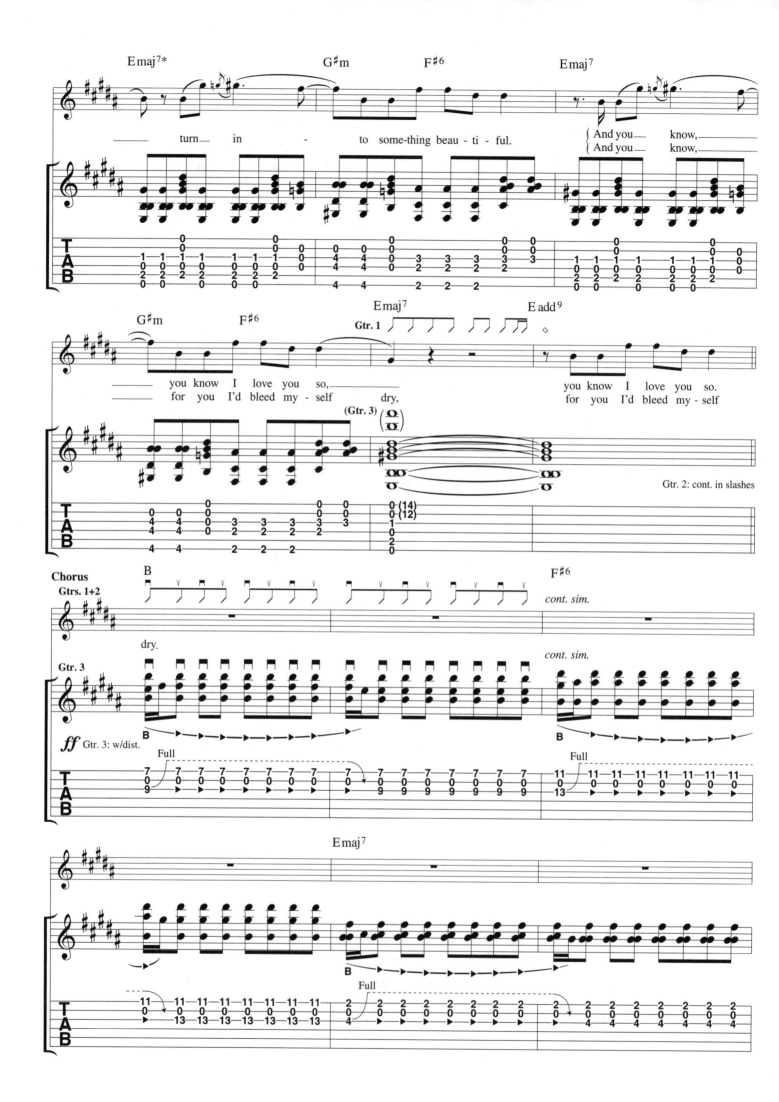

84

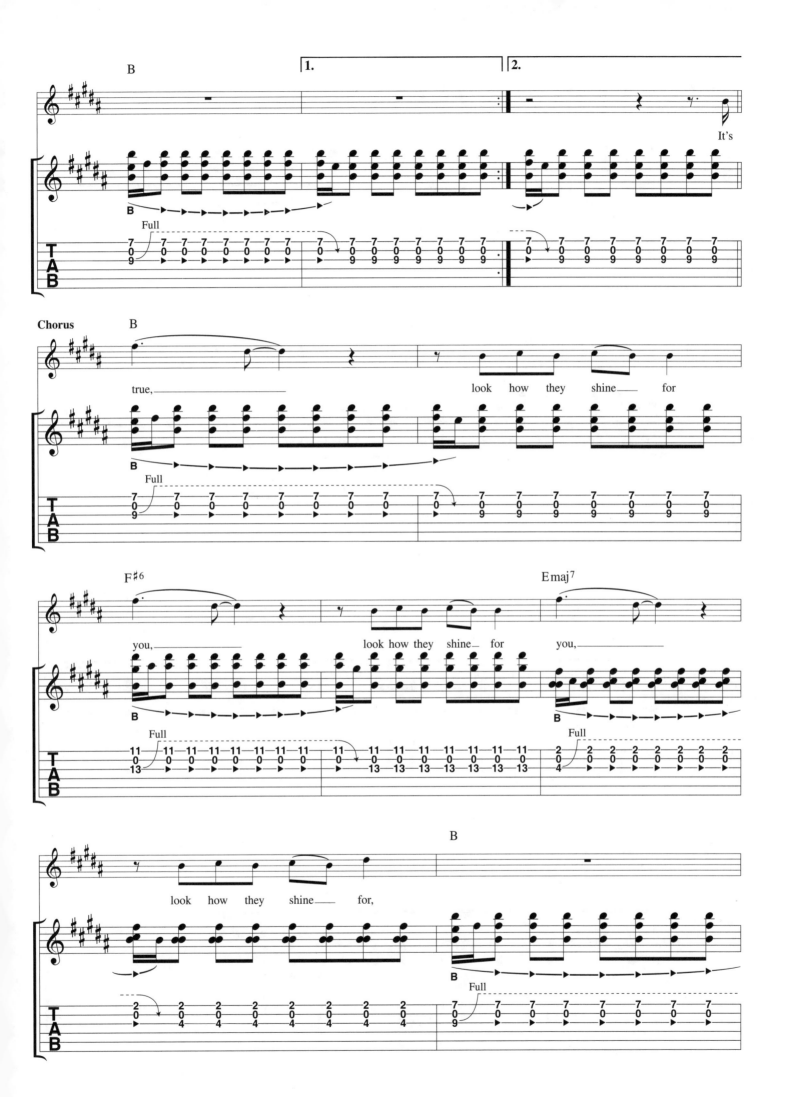

The Scientist

Words & Music by Guy Berryman, Jon Buckland, Will Champion & Chris Martin

*basic chord names

* Symbols in ( ) represent chord names with respect to capoed gtr. (Tab 0 = capo 1st fret)
Symbols above represent actual sounding chords.

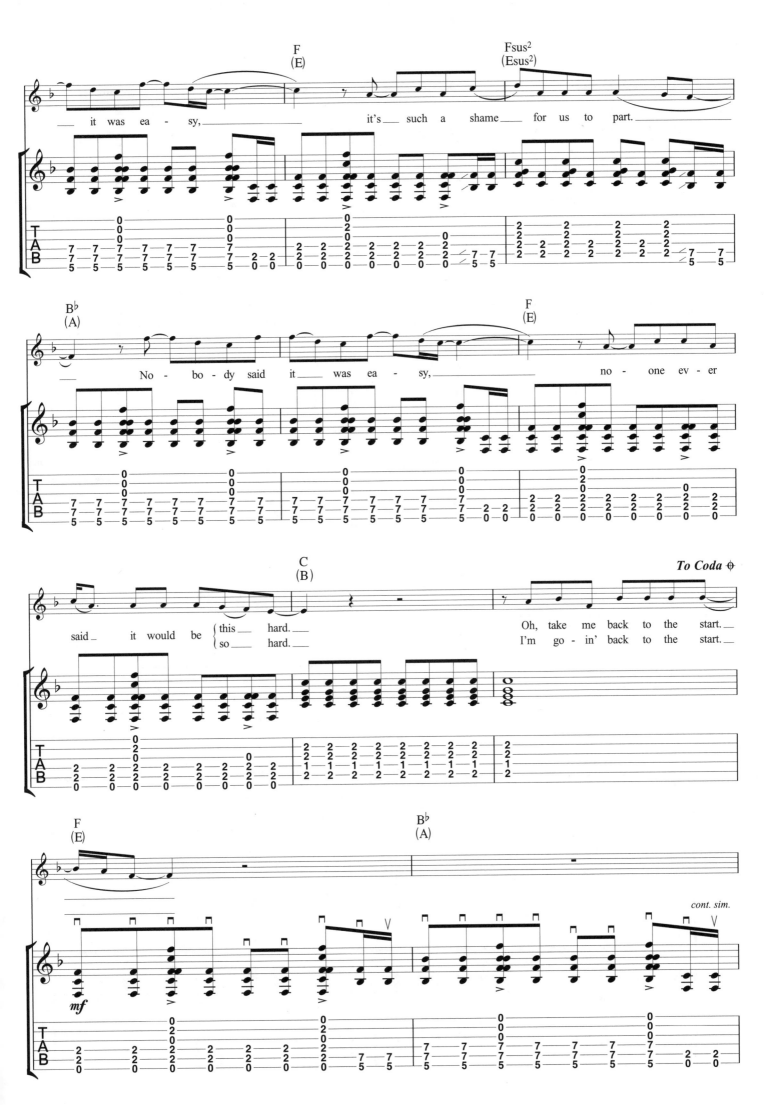

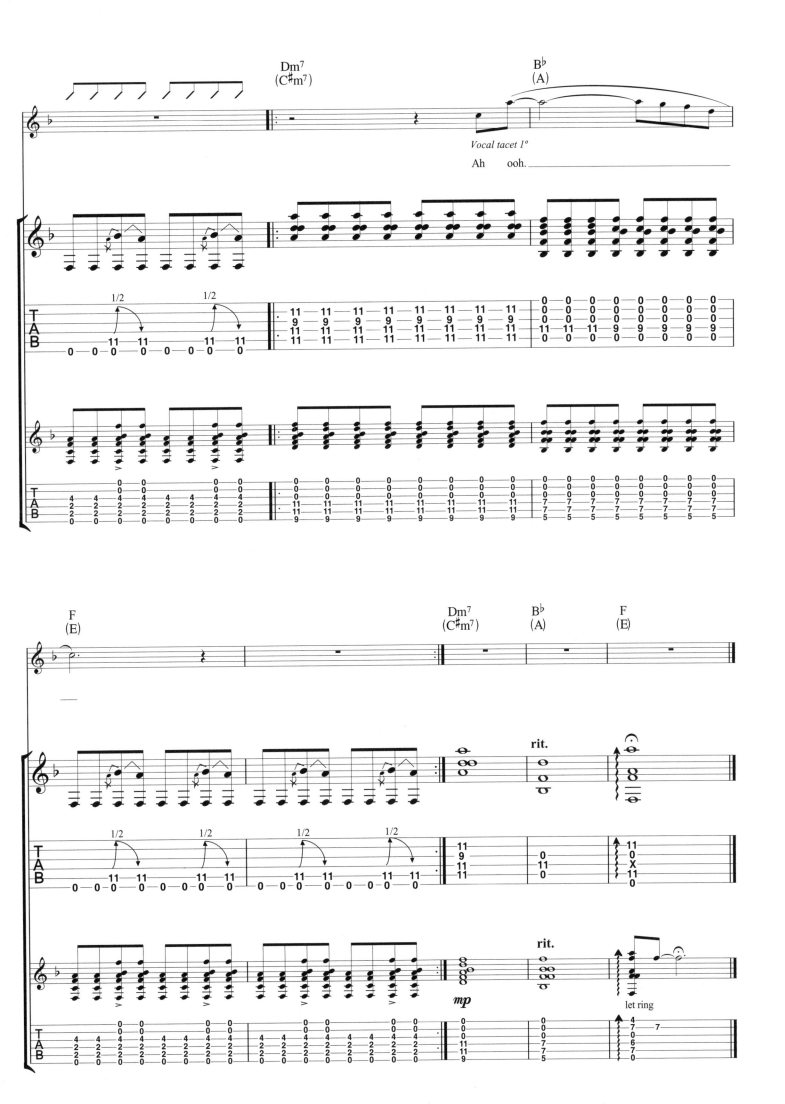

Clocks

Words & Music by Guy Berryman, Jon Buckland, Will Champion & Chris Martin

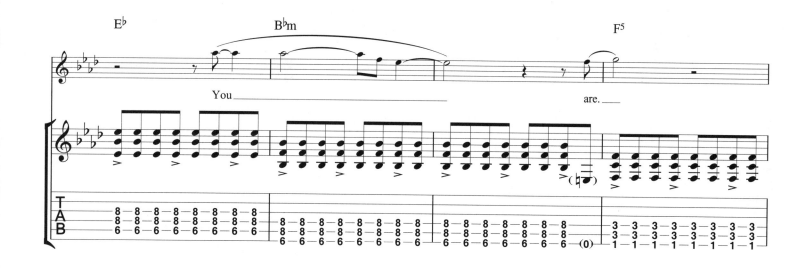

You_____ are. ____

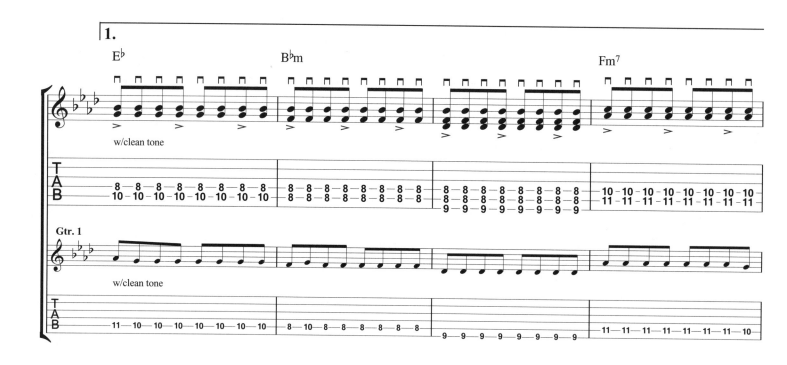

1.

w/clean tone

Gtr. 1

w/clean tone

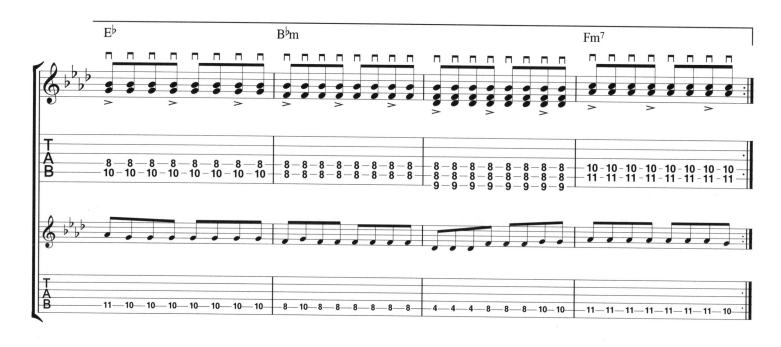

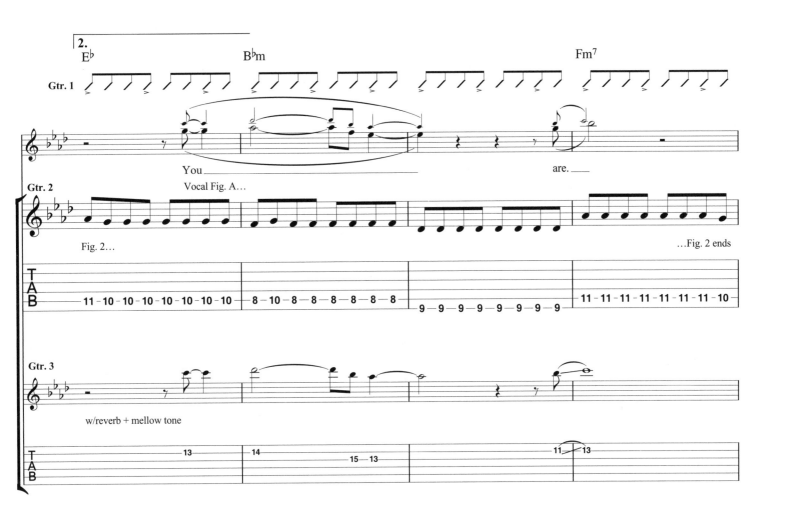

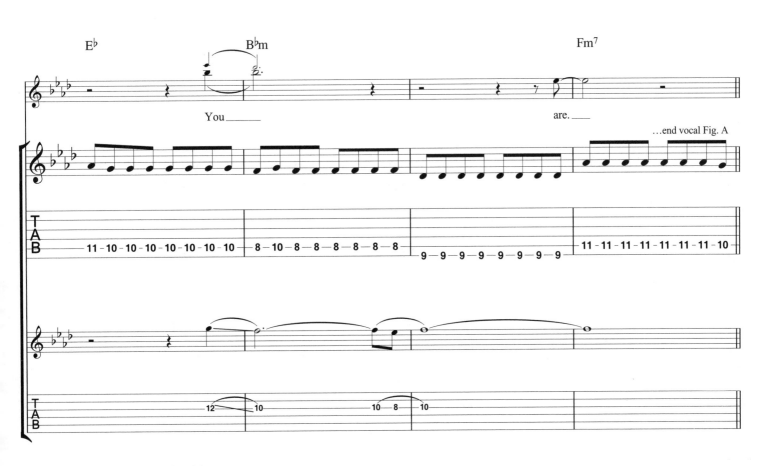

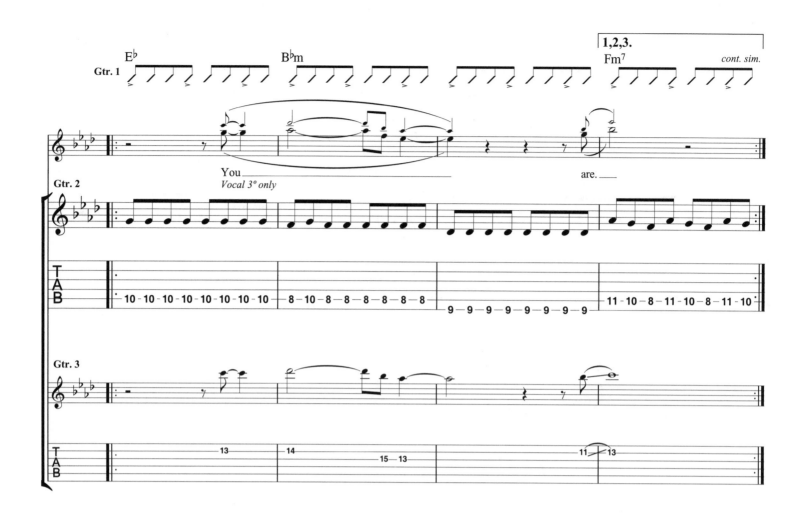

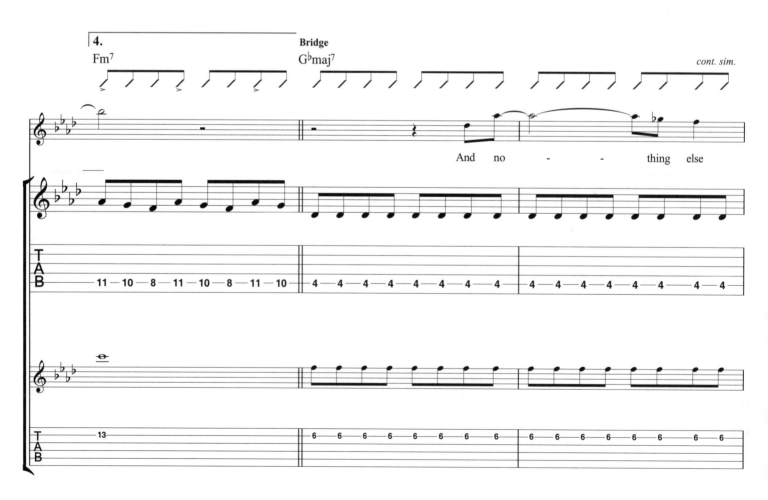

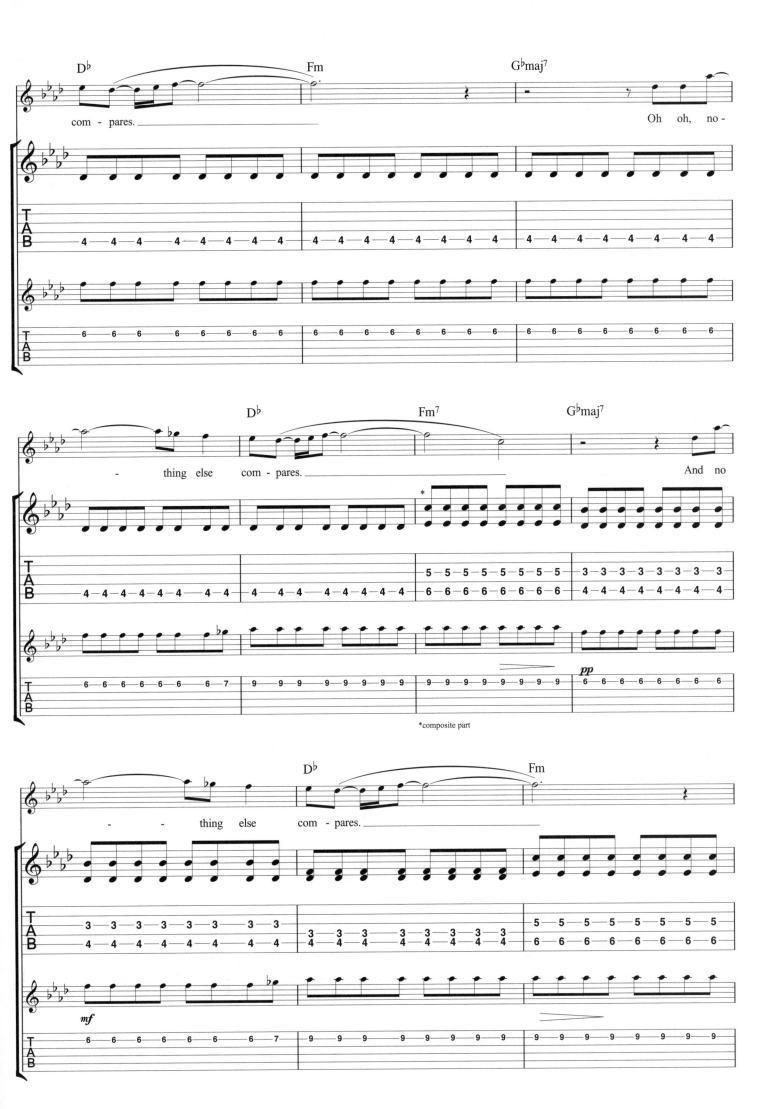

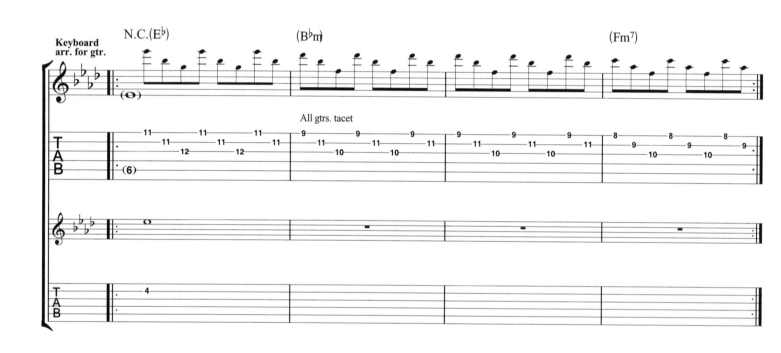

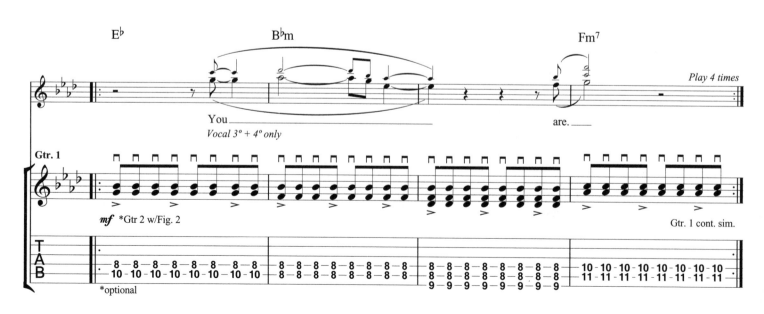

In My Place

Words & Music by Guy Berryman, Jon Buckland, Will Champion & Chris Martin

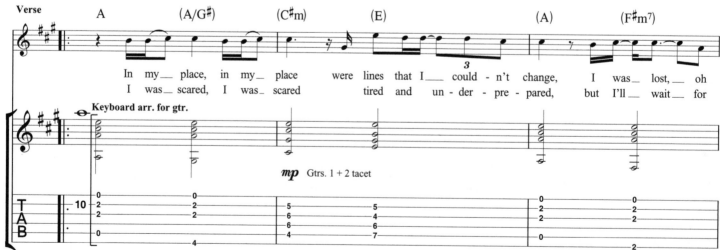

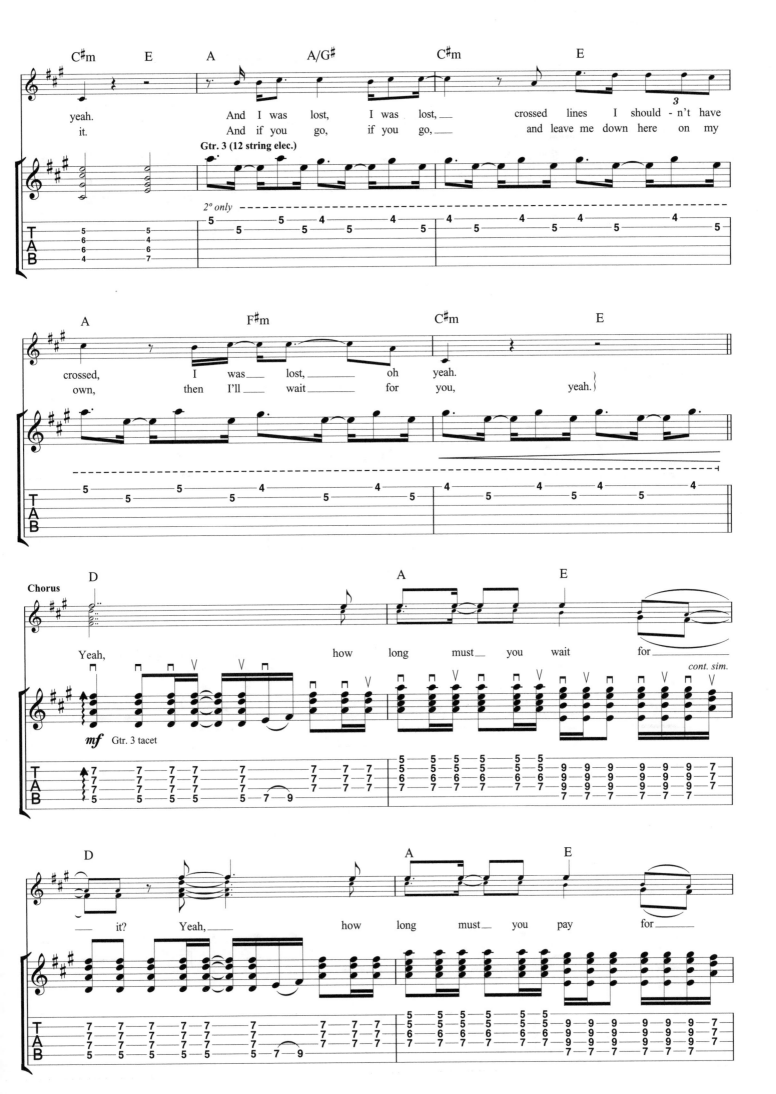

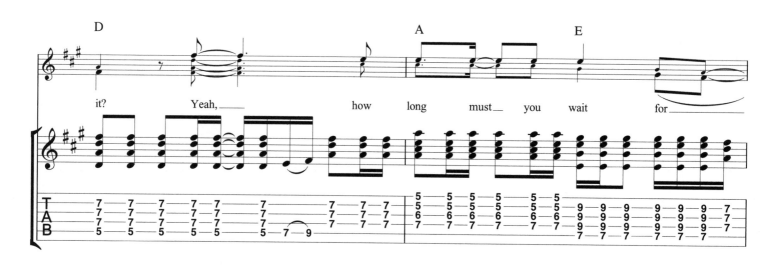

it?   Yeah,____   how   long   must__   you   wait   for____

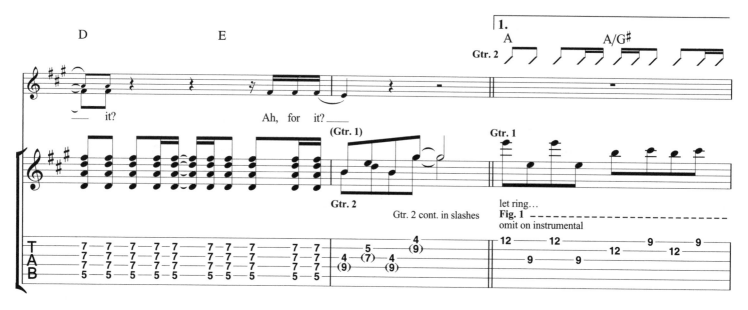

____ it?   Ah, for   it?____

Gtr. 2 cont. in slashes

Fig. 1 − − − − − − − − − −
omit on instrumental

let ring…

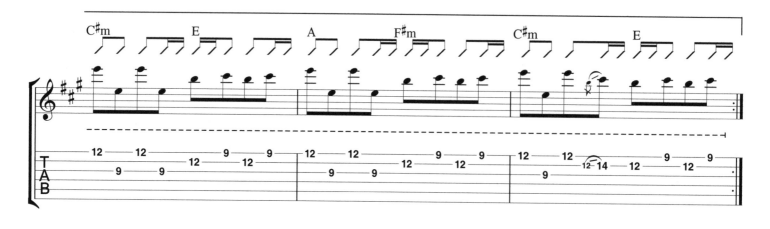

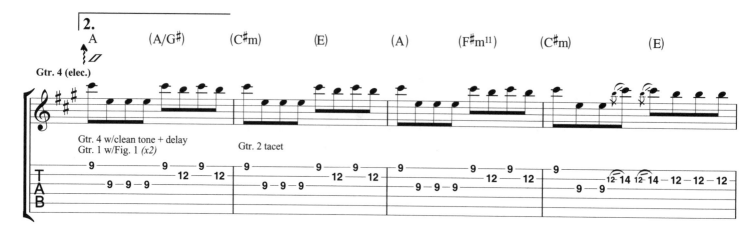

Gtr. 4 (elec.)

Gtr. 4 w/clean tone + delay
Gtr. 1 w/Fig. 1 *(x2)*

Gtr. 2 tacet

Amsterdam

Words & Music by Guy Berryman, Jon Buckland, Will Champion & Chris Martin

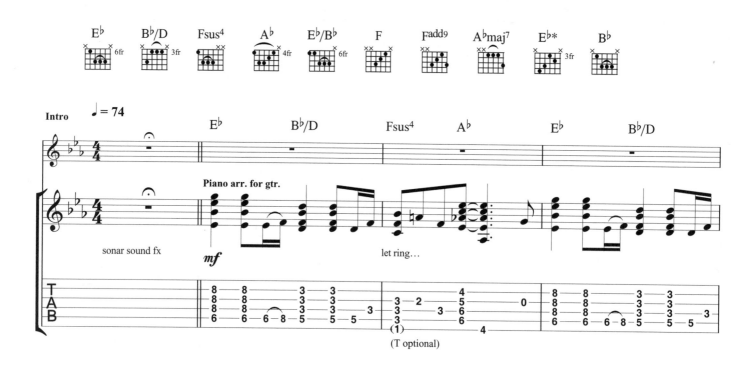

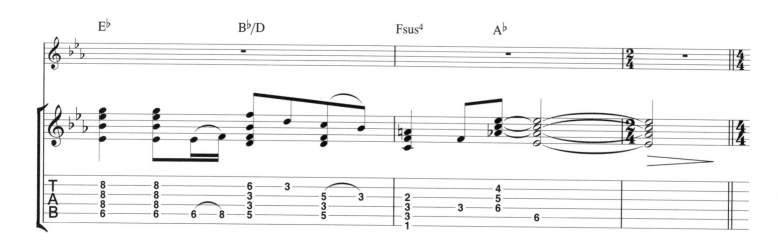

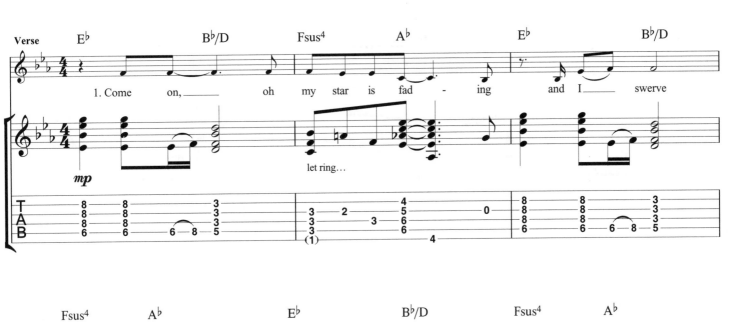

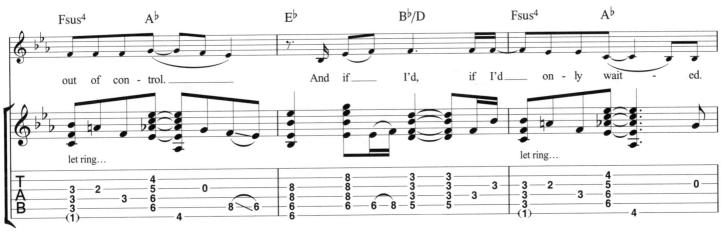

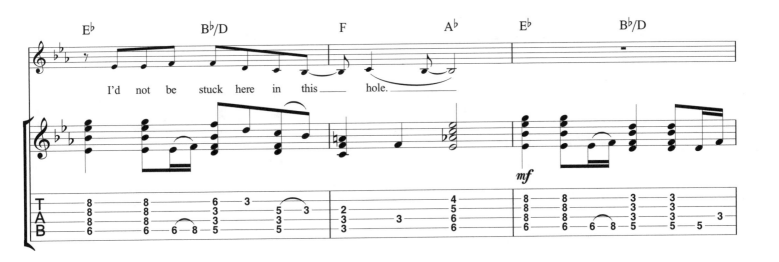

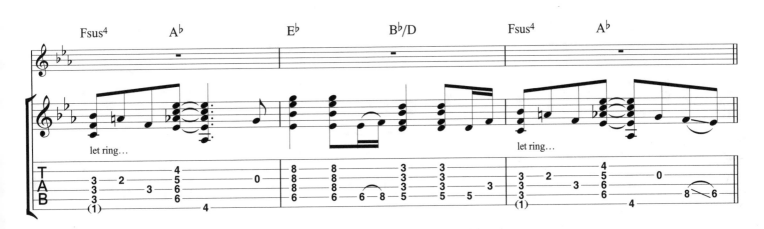

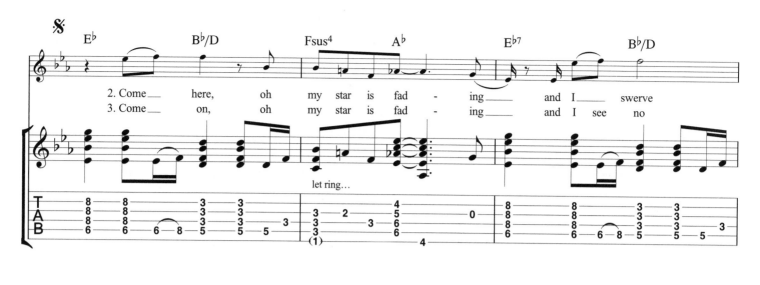

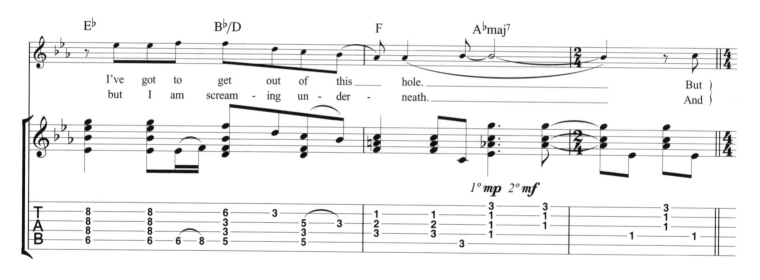

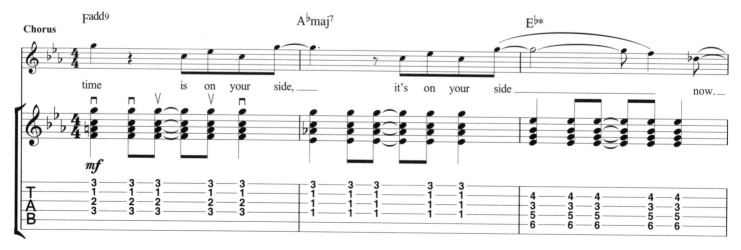

I'm push - ing you down ___ and all a - round, ___ it's no cause

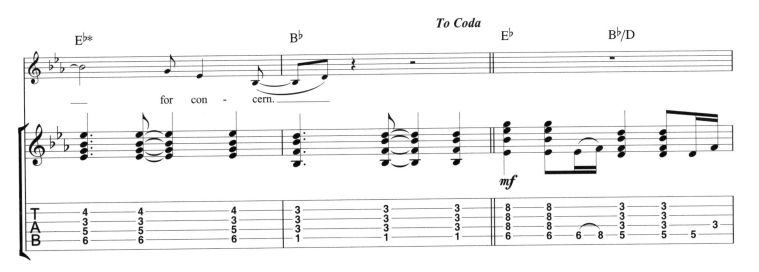

for con - cern.

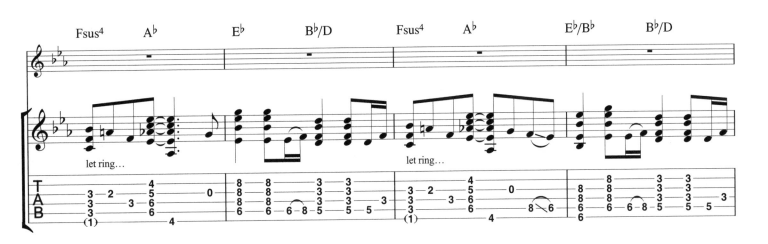

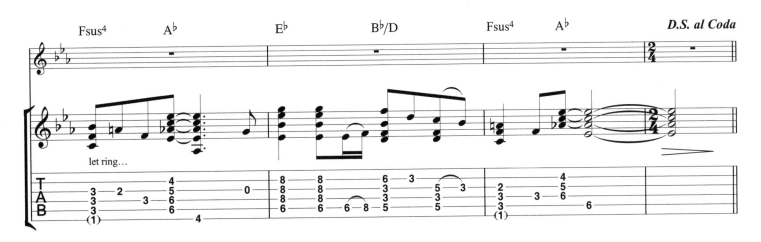

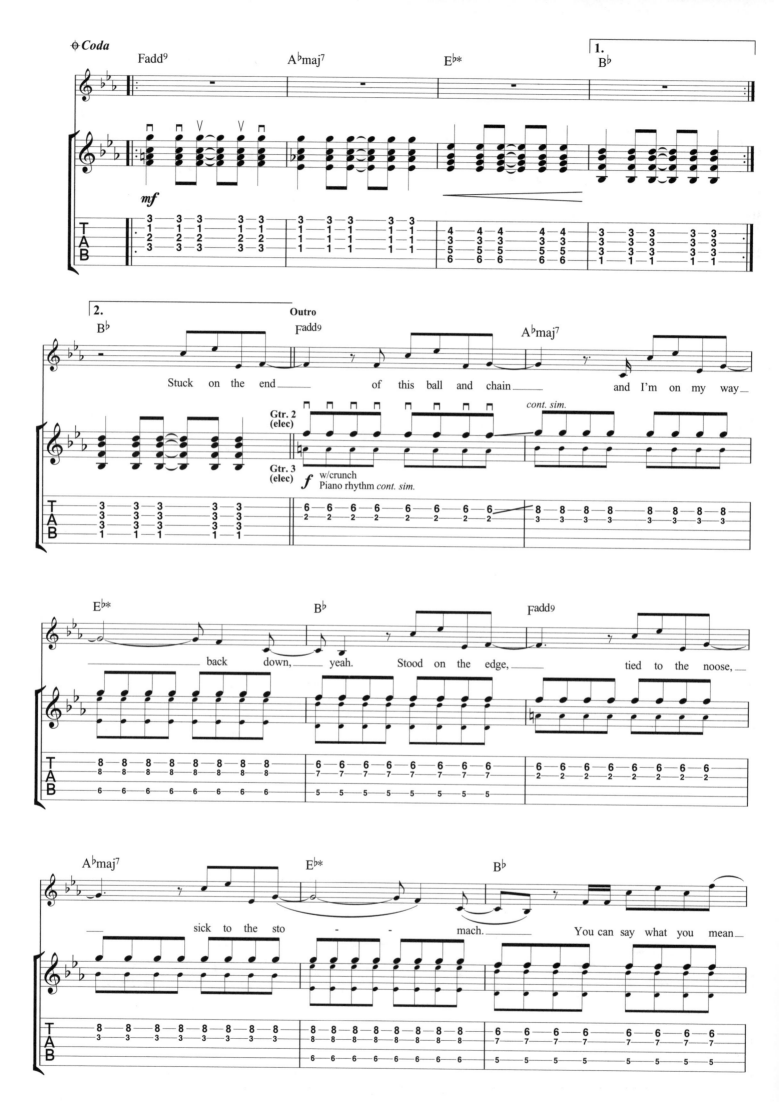

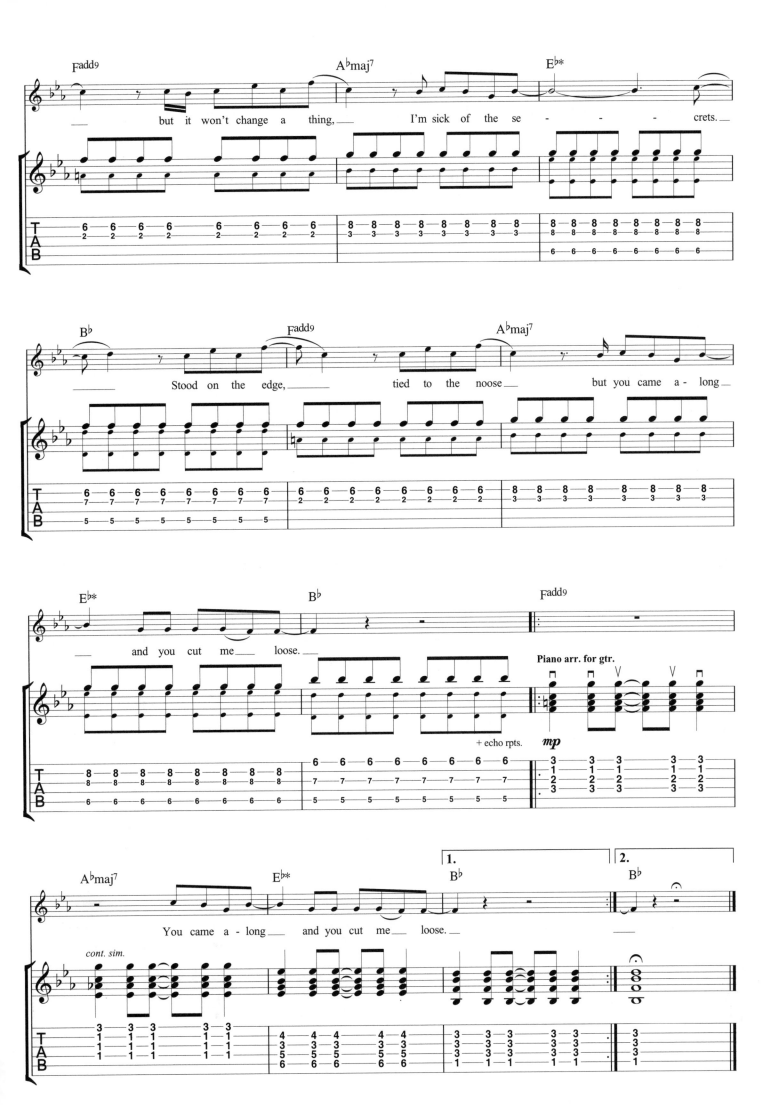

Life Is For Living

Words & Music by Guy Berryman, Jon Buckland, Will Champion & Chris Martin

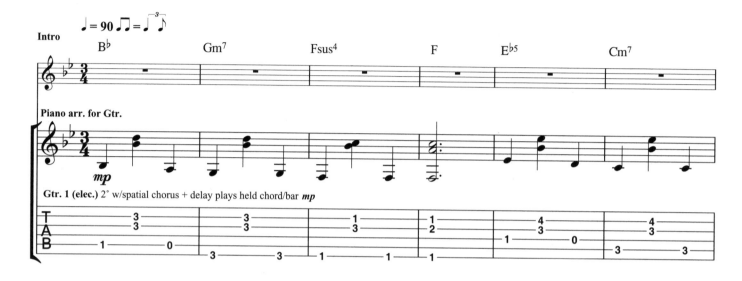

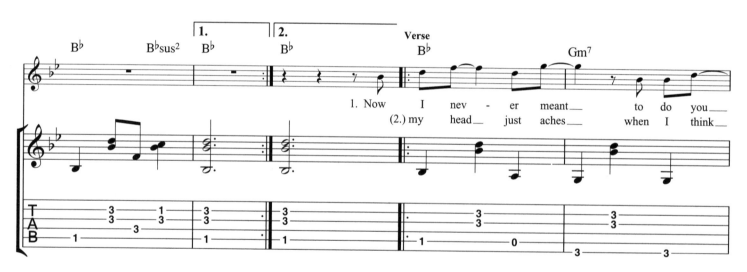

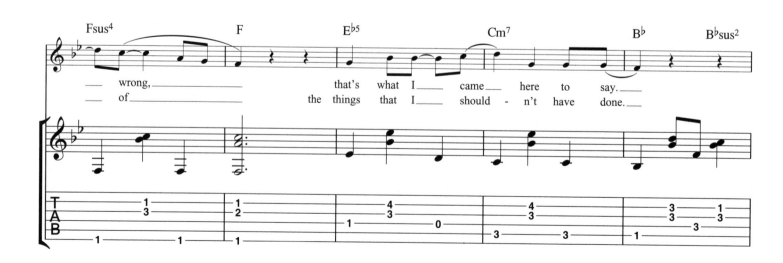